CHINESE EXPORT PORCELAIN

from the Ethel (Mrs. Julius) Liebman and
Arthur L. Liebman Porcelain Collection

Donated to the Elvehjem Museum
by Mr. and Mrs. John C. Cleaver

BY CATHERINE COLEMAN BRAWER

Elvehjem Museum of Art
University of Wisconsin–Madison
1992

Elvehjem Museum of Art
The University of Wisconsin–Madison
800 University Avenue
Madison, Wisconsin 53706–1479

ISBN 932900–30–5

Library of Congress Catalog Number 92–052695

Cover: A mug for the English market, ca. 1780, with two
    figures, hands joined, before an altar of love (see
    catalogue number 48).

Edited by Patricia Powell
Designed by Earl Madden
Produced by University Publications
Printed in Hong Kong

TABLE OF CONTENTS

Europe Trades with China   7

The *Fan-kuei* at Guangzhou   17

The Kilns at Jingdezhen   27

The Shapes of Export Porcelain   28

Armorial Porcelain   30

Pseudo-armorial Devices   65

Western Designs and Techniques   94

Indigenous Eastern Designs   146

Endnotes   155

Bibliography   157

LIST OF FIGURES

Figure 1: Cross-section of the storage area of an East
    India Company ship packed with export china   7

Figure 2: Spode plate with central arms of
    East India Company   20

Figure 3: Reverse of Spode plate   20

Figure 4: Pair of tureens   28

Figure 5: Three teapots   28

Figure 6: Two tea caddies   29

Figure 7: Tea bowl, saucer, and coffee cup   29

Figure 8: Coffee can and saucer   29

Figure 9: Reverse of catalogue number 33   57

Figure 10: Reverse of catalogue number 69   95

Figure 11: Meissen saucer with chinoiserie   106

COLOR PLATES

Color Plate I   10

Color Plate II   11

Color Plate III   12

Color Plate IV   13

Color Plate V   14

Color Plate VI   15

Color Plate VII   16

Publication of this handbook has been made possible through the generosity of The Evjue Foundation, Inc./ The Capital Times

Color plates were made possible by a grant from the Ida and William Rosenthal Foundation

Original photography by David Spradling at the time of the porcelain donation was supported by a grant from Mr. and Mrs. John C. Cleaver; additional photography by Radlund and Associates, Inc. for the catalogue was supported by the grant from The Evjue Foundation, Inc./The Capital Times

FOREWORD

The Elvehjem's Liebman Collection of Porcelains was begun and assembled in large measure by Ethel (Mrs. Julius) Liebman of Milwaukee in the first half of this century. Her son Arthur, inheriting her passion and discerning eye, continued to add to the collection until 1973 when he sold it in its entirety to Mr. and Mrs. John C. Cleaver, also of Milwaukee, with the understanding that it would be donated to the Elvehjem Museum of Art. The Cleavers physically transferred the collection to the museum and donated a portion of it immediately; the remainder was bequeathed to the museum by Mrs. Cleaver in 1991, Mr. Cleaver having passed away in 1975. The collection, by mutual consent, is named not after the museum's benefactors but rather after the original collectors whose personal taste and collecting activity it represents.

The entire Liebman collection consists of approximately six-hundred pieces and includes an unusually wide variety of objects and styles, many of which have been judged to be of outstanding quality. Numbering three hundred and forty-eight, Chinese export porcelains constitute one of its strongest and most complete areas. However, the present catalogue includes only a selection of the finest Chinese export porcelains intended for the European and American markets. Since they were also among the first objects donated to the Elvehjem by the Cleavers, it seemed particularly appropriate to begin the publication of the collection with this particular group.

Among the earliest objects in this outstanding group of Chinese export porcelains are a blue-and-white plate with a Rotterdam riot scene produced for the Dutch market (ca. 1690–95) and a shallow blue-and-white bowl with a French scene for the French market (ca. 1700–10). There are several comparative examples of teapots from different periods of the eighteenth century, as well as a rich assortment of plates with designs derived from popular prints and watch cases as well as important armorial services. Most of the well-known European designs are included in the collection, along with a few individual examples not found elsewhere.

As one of the most extensive collections of Chinese export porcelain for the European market in the United States, the Liebman collection is an important resource not only for the University of Wisconsin, but for collectors, scholars, and students of Chinese, European, and commercial history, as well as the history of European and American decorative arts throughout the country.

The catalogue was originally conceived by then-director Millard F. Rogers, Jr. (now director of the Cincinnati Art Museum) who in 1974 invited Catherine Coleman Brawer, a then-member of the Elvehjem staff, to research the collection, document the individual pieces, and place them in their historical context. Although Ms. Brawer completed her work by the time she moved to New York in 1976, for a variety of reasons, lack of funding chief among them, her valuable research has remained unpublished until the present time.

Ms. Brawer's research reemerged in the course of the building renovations of 1989–90. As part of the overall reinstallation plan, new niche cases were designed for the first permanent display of the museum's porcelains. To assist with the selection of objects for display from the Liebman Collection, I sought out Ms. Brawer's archived materials and found them to be an excellent guide. In the spring of 1990, Catherine Brawer herself returned to Madison and graciously curated a permanent installation of Chinese Export porcelains from the Liebman Collection for the museum. She also updated her original text in preparation for the present volume based on her most recent studies. The museum truly owes a debt of gratitude to Ms. Brawer for her unflagging efforts to document this collection and for her patience in waiting for its publication.

The museum's deepest appreciation must also be extended to the Evjue Foundation, Inc. / The Capital Times, which in 1991 generously stepped into the breach of years to underwrite this publication. Without the munificent support of the Evjue Foundation the present volume would not have been possible, and this most important collection would remain relatively unknown except to those who happened upon it during a visit to Madison. Additional funds to print color plates were provided by the Ida and William Rosenthal Foundation.

As always no project could go forward without the assistance of an excellent staff. Particularly, I want to acknowledge Patricia Powell for editing the catalogue and facilitating its production in every way. Museum registrar Lindy Waites and registrar Sandy Rogers arranged for a significant portion of the photography; assistant director for administration Corinne Magnoni most efficiently coordinated various practical matters, while Lori DeMeuse kept the museum's accounts in good order.

On behalf of the museum, I also wish to thank UW Publications, especially Earl Madden for the design of the catalogue and Linda Kietzer for coordinating its pro-

duction. Photography for this publication was initially carried out by David Spradling and later completed by Radlund and Associates, Inc., of Madison.

Finally, we must thank Mr. and Mrs. John C. Cleaver for their generous and thoughtful gift. The Liebman collection is an outstanding resource which will benefit students and museum visitors for generations to come.

Russell Panczenko
Director
Spring 1992

AUTHOR'S ACKNOWLEDGMENTS

I would like to thank the following people who gave so generously of their time to help with the catalogue: Millard F. Rogers, Jr., who conceived the project; David Howard, who read the original catalogue entries; David Spradling, who took many of the excellent photographs; and these who answered my questions: John Austin, Christine Boot, Callie Efird, Kathryn G. Farnham, Clare Le Corbeiller, and Ronald Lightbown. William Bunce, director of the Kohler Art Library, and his staff did everything possible to facilitate research on the collection. I also want to thank director Russell Panczenko for reviving the project and editor Patricia Powell for her help in coordinating photograph and manuscript production. Last, I am indebted to Geri Wu for her expert and unstinting assistance in revising the manuscript.

I fell in love with Chinese export porcelain almost twenty years ago while researching pieces in the Liebman collection. I hope that the publication of this catalogue will give the collection, one of the few in America to concentrate on porcelain for the European market, the recognition it deserves.

Catherine Coleman Brawer
New York, New York
January, 1992

In measuring the porcelain we have rounded to the nearest eighth of an inch and given the precise number for centimeters.

EUROPE TRADES WITH CHINA

By the time Europe began to trade actively with China in the sixteenth century, China had already been involved in trading silk, tea, spices, and porcelain throughout Asia and the Middle East for almost nine hundred years.[1] Porcelain itself was never considered an inherently valuable commodity. As trade between Europe and China increased during the eighteenth century, porcelain continued to be imported into Europe primarily because it served as clean and protective ballast over which the more delicate cargo of silks, tea, and spices could be safely packed. Even as the number of porcelains imported by the West increased into the millions, it continued to play a relatively minor role in the China trade.

The Portuguese were the first Europeans to go to China in search of spices. When they arrived in 1515, they found a highly organized system of transport and communication that the Chinese had developed over centuries of exporting their goods to Southeast Asia and the Near East. The Portuguese also found a centuries' old suspicion of foreigners and soon learned that, although the Chinese wanted to profit from trade with the West, they would not allow foreigners to venture into China any farther than was necessary for them to conduct their business. A Portuguese expedition of 1517 ignored this restriction by proceeding without permission up the Pearl River to Guangzhou (Canton) and firing what the Portuguese considered to be a respectful cannon salute. To the Chinese, the sound of the cannons was terrifying and merely confirmed all of their worst suspicions about foreign traders. Although the Portuguese captain was able to mollify the Chinese, with the result that his ship sailed away laden with goods, the stage had been set for a difficult relationship between the Chinese and European traders. Subsequent acts of Portuguese piracy led the Chinese to close the port of Guangzhou to foreign shipping, and it was not reopened until the end of the seventeenth century. In the meantime, the Portuguese needed a base from which to conduct their Asian trade and by 1557 had established themselves in Macao. From Macao they were allowed to trade at Guangzhou twice a year. Until England and Holland entered the competition in 1600,

Portugal had a virtual monopoly on the porcelain trade throughout Asia.

Like the Portuguese, the English and Dutch went to China in search of spices, not porcelain. Successful voyages soon led to the founding of the British East India Company in 1600, but because the British received little governmental support, the Dutch were soon able to supplant them and to wrest Oriental trade from the Portuguese. The Dutch decision to challenge the Portuguese trade monopoly was necessitated by the political situation in 1594, when Spain was at war with Holland, and Philip II, ruler of both Portugal and Spain, closed

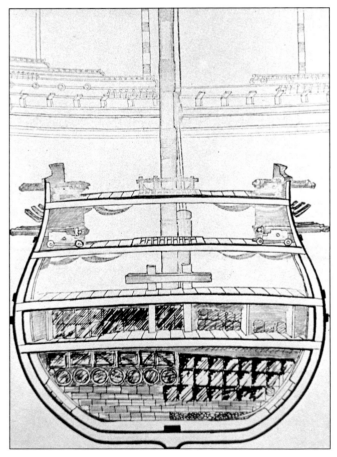

Fig. 1. Cross-section of the storage area of an East India ship packed with export china. Courtesy of Spode Limited, England.

the port of Lisbon to Dutch shipping. In order to obtain goods from China at reasonable prices, the Dutch formed the Dutch East India Company in 1602. Its vessels were equipped to trade or fight as necessary, commanded by captains who held unlimited power.

That same year, the Dutch captured a Portuguese ship, the *S. Jago*, and auctioned the ship's contents, including quantities of blue-and-white porcelain, in Middleburgh, Holland. Two years later the Dutch captured another Portuguese ship, the *Sta. Catharina*, which carried as part of its cargo approximately 100,000 pieces of blue-and-white porcelain. This porcelain was successfully auctioned in Amsterdam to buyers from all over Europe, including the kings of England and France.[2]

With the European market in mind, the Dutch expanded their trade with China, making Batavia (present-day Jakarta) their East Asian headquarters. Unlike the Portuguese, whose main market for Chinese porcelain had been Asia, the Dutch quickly realized that the best way to sell Chinese porcelain in Europe was to provide the Europeans with porcelains adapted to their own taste and table customs. As early as 1635 the Dutch provided the Chinese with painted wooden models of current continental silver and pewter shapes to copy; later on they added ceramic and glass models. Until about 1770 the Dutch sent popular prints and drawings to China to be copied onto these European shapes and also employed artists to execute designs specifically for porcelain decoration.[3]

Dutch supremacy continued until the middle of the seventeenth century, by which time Holland had imported approximately three million pieces of porcelain into Europe. They successfully ousted the Portuguese from all of their East Asian bases except Macao, from which the Portuguese hung onto a small portion of

the trade by offering the Chinese protection against the numerous pirates along the Chinese coast. All Dutch trade with China ceased, however, in 1657 when internal political strife in China resulted in both the destruction of the porcelain kilns at Jingdezhen (Ching-te-Chen) and a trade embargo against the Dutch. Although the kilns were rebuilt in 1677, not until 1695 were Chinese junks again permitted to sail to Batavia to trade directly with the Dutch, as they had before the rebellion. The Dutch had no sooner reactivated their trade with China than the French arrived in 1698, and the English in the following year.

The return of the English to China after two earlier unsuccessful attempts to trade coincided with the Chinese government's decision to open the port of Guangzhou to foreign commerce. After a period of eight years, the English merged a new East India Company that had recently gained a foothold in China with the East India Company that maintained a firm position in India. The English were now strong enough to supplant the Dutch, and in 1715 they were the first East India Company granted permission to open an office in Guangzhou. The subsequent formation of the Danish East India Company in 1730 and the Swedish East India Company the following year did not threaten British supremacy, since the British market did not include Scandinavia.

From 1730 until the end of the eighteenth century, England dominated a trade with China that was actively shared at various times by France, Holland, Sweden, and Denmark. Despite the fact that spices, tea, and silk always remained the more valued commodities, over sixty million pieces of porcelain were imported into Europe. In 1784 as British influence began to decline, America entered the China trade, thereby providing a new market for export porcelain.

COLOR PLATES
I–VII

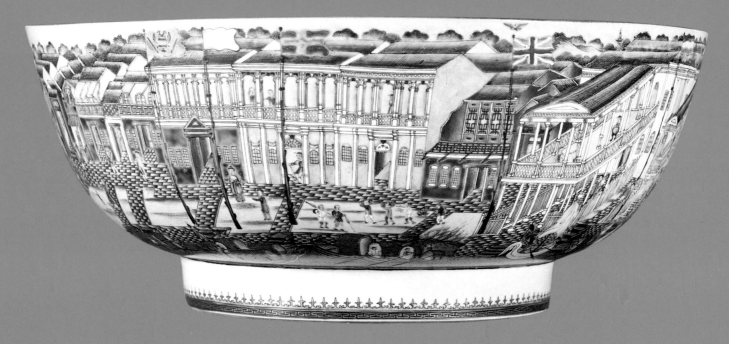

COLOR PLATE I
Catalogue number 4. A punch bowl for the European market ca. 1785, with a continuous depiction of the warehouses at Guangzhou, with the flags of Prussia, France, Sweden, England, Holland, and Denmark.

COLOR PLATE II
Catalogue number 9. An unusually large chocolate cup with unidentified coat of arms.

COLOR PLATE III
Catalogue number 43. A plate for the Danish market, ca. 1745, with a double marriage shield showing Neptune and Venus.

COLOR PLATE IV
Catalogue number 77. A plate for the Scottish market, ca. 1740–45, with a central scene of two Scottish Highlanders in kilts.

13

COLOR PLATE V
Catalogue number 85. A plate for the Dutch market, ca. 1750, showing the central scene of the Bull's Cruelty or Wonder at Zaandam.

14

COLOR PLATE VI
Catalogue number 89. A plate for the European market, ca. 1760, with the central scene of the Building of the Temple of Solomon, with King Solomon, Hiram, and Masonic symbols.

COLOR PLATE VII
Catalogue number 107. A plate for the Continental market, ca. 1750, with the central scene of the Crucifixion.

THE *FAN-KUEI* AT GUANGZHOU

The Chinese suspicion of foreigners, whom they called *fan-kuei* ("foreign devils"), continued throughout the China trade. When they opened the port of Guangzhou in 1699, the Chinese made certain that Western merchants would remain outside city walls by confining them to an area a quarter of a mile wide, facing south along the Pearl River. They further subjected the *fan-kuei* to an elaborate code of imperial regulations which the Westerners had no choice but to obey if they wished to remain in Guangzhou.

The American William C. Hunter, upon his arrival in Guangzhou in 1825, wrote that he found it much the same as it had been fifty years earlier.[4] A small area open to foreign trade contained all of the *hang* or places of business and residence of the Western merchants. On the main floor of the *hang* were warehouse facilities and dining and public rooms, with sleeping accommodations on the floor above. Because the various East India companies rented the same *hang* year after year, the national flags flying above them generally remained the same. A punch bowl in the Liebman collection (cat. no. 4) illustrates the *hang* as they looked about 1780, before the arrival of the Americans. From left to right are the flags of Prussia, France, Sweden, England, Holland, and Denmark. There were thirteen buildings in all, so that the street that ran behind the *hang* was known as Thirteen Factory Street. In the same area lived ten or twelve Chinese merchants who formed the *cohang*. Responsible to the emperor, these *hang* merchants conducted all business with the West and saw to it that imperial regulations governing Western behavior were imposed.

Imperial regulations decreed that upon arrival in China, Westerners were required to hire a pilot for their ship at Macao and proceed directly up the Pearl River thirty miles to Whampoa Anchorage at Guangzhou. There the ship was left at anchor with the crew, and a comprador was hired to supply the ship with food and any other necessities. Like the pilot, the comprador was registered at Macao and wore an identification badge around his waist. Only under his supervision were foreigners permitted to communicate with the Chinese. In order to control smuggling, the imperial regulations forbade foreigners to "rove about the bays at pleasure and sell to rascally natives goods subject to duty, that these may smuggle them, and thereby defraud His Celestial Majesty's revenue."[5]

The imperial revenue was continually augmented by taxes and bribes exacted from Westerners for doing business in China as soon as their ship anchored at Whampoa. A linguist or interpreter was then engaged, as well as a *hang* merchant to purchase the ship's cargo. The selection of this merchant by the supercargo, or business agent of the voyage, was critical. As American Dudley Pickman, Jr. wrote to Benjamin Shreve of Salem about 1815:

> The most important thing in your voyage is in securing your ship. You had better not employ a Man of doubtful Character *at any rate*. Engage with a security merchant of the first Character even at rather higher prices for your goods and you will be sure to have a good cargo and without being delayed beyond the time stipulated for. There are generally about 12 security merchants, with one of whom you must engage (sic) of those who were in the Hong in 1805, when I was at Canton, 5 or 6 did much American Business.[6]

The supercargoes circulated among themselves descriptions of the different merchants. Houqua, for one, was considered dependable; Ponqua, "too poor to deal with"; and Consequa, "a very uncertain man."[7] Strictly regulated by the Chinese authorities, these merchants had to pay numerous petty bribes to government officials in Beijing. Some were able to amass a considerable fortune nonetheless. The trusted merchant Houqua is said to have retired early in the nineteenth century with twenty-six million dollars. Even at the height of his career, however, he had no power against the Chinese authorities.

In securing the cargo for a Western ship, the *hang* merchant functioned as a middleman. He was neither a decorator nor a manufacturer of porcelain, but a supplier who kept in his Guangzhou warehouse stock patterns known to be popular in the West. He also kept a supply of undecorated wares that could be enameled on short notice by local porcelain decorators in He-nan. Although these stock patterns comprised the bulk of the China trade, a *hang* merchant could special-order fine quality porcelains with armorial or individualized decorations by traveling to Jingdezhen, where the porcelain was manufactured. Special-ordering a service was a matter of luck; the supercargo could only hope that it would be decorated exactly as his client in Europe had requested and that the entire service would arrive in Guangzhou in good condition before he sailed.[8]

The supercargo was responsible for the financial success of a voyage. Each one had to be a banker with a knowledge of foreign exchange, a diplomat able to deal with any number of bizarre situations that might arise, and a merchant able to assess the relative profitability of tea and raw silks in the home market. Besides their normal stipend as public servants, the English supercargoes received "an 'Allowance' (profits from a portion of the stock on the ship), a 'Permission' (the right to export on their own certain amounts in silver and to return home with their investment in gold), and a 'Privilege' (entitling them to carry on a private trade both on the outward and the homeward trip)."[9] G. M. Pitt, chief supercargo on the *Macclesfield* in 1724, reportedly earned 5,890 pounds sterling for his round-trip voyage to Guangzhou.[10] It was thus that the East India companies lured the best possible men into the China trade.

While the orders were being filled, the East India company men remained confined to the *hang* area. They were permitted an infrequent night out, according to the imperial regulations:

[O]n the 8th, 18th, and 28th days of the moon these foreign barbarians may visit the Flower Gardens and Honan Joss-house, but not in droves of over ten at one time. When they have "refreshed" they must return to the Factories, not be allowed to pass the night "out," or collect together to carouse.[11]

Westerners therefore coveted invitations to the houses and gardens of the wealthier *hang* merchants at He-nan. During the daytime, the sailors occupied themselves by visiting local workshops. A history written in 1797 of a voyage by Charpentier-Cossigny records the following:

Every day we went to see the different Canton merchants; mostly we went into the embroiderer's workshops, or sought out the men who paint porcelain. They decorate on the biscuit and then cover with glaze. If you want to have pieces copied from European designs, they must go to Ching-te-Chen, but in that case you have to wait a year for the next voyage. For sailors who cannot afford to wait, white pieces can be bought and

painted on the spot. The painting is applied over the glaze and fired on in the kiln. Afterwards it stands out in slight relief. You can remove it with a diamond.[12]

In answer to the sailors' demands for souvenirs, the Chinese decorated porcelain with Western ship designs and various harbors and ports passed en route to Guangzhou. Known for their skill in copying, the Chinese commonly took their designs from contemporary paintings and sketches, rather than from nature. In fact, the depiction of the *hang* on the Liebman punch bowl (cat. no. 4) was probably taken from a painting done several years before the bowl was made. Renderings of ships bearing the flags of different nations were actually mass-produced without the flags, which were added later at the request of the buyer. A bowl in the Liebman collection (cat. no. 6) flying the Swedish flag might just as well have been sold to a British sailor, with his own flag substituted. Two pieces in the Liebman collection (cat. nos. 1 and 3) are decorated with Capetown Harbor, showing Table Mountain in the background. Capetown Harbor, under Dutch rule, was the midway point on the six-month voyage from Europe to China. After having sailed past the Azores and Cape Verde Islands and down the west coast of Africa, various East India companies stopped there to take on fresh food and water. From Capetown, the voyage to Macao continued across the Indian Ocean, through either the Straits of Sunda or the Straits of Malacca.

When the Americans entered the China trade in 1784, their route was determined by their cargo. Until their independence they had traded with the British West Indies, but once excluded from this British market, they needed to find new trade outlets and therefore turned to China. Partly because they had no silver to trade, the Americans were forced to use all available resources to best advantage. They gathered ginseng, a root believed by the Chinese to have medicinal powers, from the woods of New England; sandalwood from Hawaii; and sea slugs, used by the Chinese for soup, from the South Pacific. In addition they traded animal skins from the Pacific Northwest for as much as one hundred dollars apiece in Guangzhou. John Jacob Astor, owner of the American Fur Company, amassed a fortune of twenty-million dollars by his death in 1848, largely through his trade with China from 1808 to 1834.[13] Although the Americans entered the China trade gradually, state by state, it was not long before they became second to the English. Their ships were smaller but faster, and unlike the British East India Company men, the Americans owned their own ships, without any monopolistic restrictions. As America became more active, the British East India Company gradually withdrew, ceasing to import porcelain altogether by 1801. By 1834, when the British Crown withdrew its monopoly, the Americans were able to compete successfully with the independent British traders.

Other European countries had also decreased their involvement in the China trade by this time, in part because the output of their home factories had begun to rival Chinese wares in quality and cost. The Europeans had long been interested in producing porcelain themselves and, in 1708, the centuries-old Chinese secret was discovered in Germany. The alchemist Johann Friedrich Boettger, working at Meissen, carried out a series of experiments to test the heat resistance and chemical changes of Saxon earths and minerals at high temperatures. By mixing refractory clay with fusible earths, he soon developed a hard, red stoneware, and by substituting the recently discovered white clay, kaolin, for the red earth in the stoneware, Boettger was able to produce a porcelain similar to that manufactured in China. From 1713 the factories at Meissen were producing porcelain; other European countries were soon to follow, as factories were established at Vienna in 1719 and Venice in 1720. The Royal French Factory at Sèvres rose in prominence after mid-century, and hard-paste porcelain was first manufactured in England at the Plymouth factory in 1768. The Spode factory, which added the manufacture of porcelain about 1800, is credited with establishing the composition that has become standard English bone-porcelain. The extent to which Britain enjoyed a self-sufficiency in the manufacture of porcelain is evidenced by the fact that when the East India Company warehouse in Guangzhou was destroyed by fire in 1823, an order to replace a 1300-piece service originally manufactured in Guangzhou, was given to the Spode factory in England. This service, which bears the East India Company arms, is similar to two plates in the Liebman collection (fig. 2), which are probably contemporaneous. They were perhaps for use aboard the East India Company ship *The London*, which is thought to have sailed from London to Guangzhou with the Spode service, as the name of the ship is marked on the back (fig. 3).

Fig. 3
Reverse of Spode plate

Fig. 2
PLATE, molded gadroon edge.
On reverse: "SPODE, FELDSPAR
   PORCELAIN, THE LONDON"
English, Spode factory
Feldspar porcelain, ca. 1824
Diam. 9 1/8 in. (23.2 cm.)
1975.177 a

Central arms of East India Company sur-mounted by crest. Two gold lion sup-porters stand on green plinth above a banderole inscribed *AUSPICIO REGIS ET SENATUS ANGLIAE*, holding East India Company banners. Inner gold band. Three floral sprays in relief, detailed in gold. Outer gadroon border.

This plate, one of a pair in the Liebman Collection, is similar to those which replaced a service of 1300 pieces that was destroyed when the East India Company warehouse in Guangzhou burned in 1823. The inscription "The London" on the reverse of each plate (fig. 3) suggests that they were possibly ordered by Captain John Barnet Sotherby, who sailed a ship of that name from England to Guangzhou in March of

1824, possibly with the East India Company service. The Liebman plates may have been for his personal use aboard ship.[14]

The manufacture of these plates in England rather than in China shows not only the decline in trade between the two countries, but the ability of the Spode factory to reproduce at a competitive price patterns that had previously been manufactured in Guangzhou. The body of the feldspar porcelain is white and translucent, qualities which had been sought by Staffordshire potters throughout the eighteenth century in imitation of true Chinese porcelain.

Illustration of similar plates in *Spode*, pl. 164 and Howard, p. 66.

1
BOWL
Dutch market, ca. 1740–50
Diam. 4⅝ in. (11.3 cm.)
1974.59

Continuous scene of Dutch ships in Capetown Harbor with Table Mountain, Dutch buildings, and flags. All in shades of green, blue, brown, iron red, black, and gold. Gold line edged in black on interior rim; black floral spray in center.

Although Capetown Harbor was used as a stopover by several East India companies, this composition is known only with Dutch flags.[15] Compare this early version with that on a later teapot (cat. no. 3), where Table Mountain is no longer flat but rounded.

Illustration of plate with the same scene and a Meissen-inspired lacework border in *Patterns*, pl. 33.

2
COFFEE CUP and SAUCER
English market, ca. 1750
Cup: H. 2¼ in. (5.7 cm.)
Saucer: Diam. 4¾ in. (12 cm.)
1975.98 a, b

All-over scene of the Sailor's Farewell, with a Western landscape and a ship flying the East India Company flag awaiting in the harbor. All in puce with gold rim. Iron-red highlights on the saucer.

The Sailor's Farewell was a popular design on both Chinese export porcelain and English ceramics. Although the original for this design has not been traced, the careful painting clearly fol-lows a European engraving. On both the cup and saucer, painted by two different artists, the woman weeps and clings to the sailor, unlike more stylized versions in which the emotion is lacking.

A polychrome version derived from the same original with an elaborate border is illustrated in Scheurleer, cat. 248.

3
TEAPOT
Dutch market, ca. 1770
Diam. 5½ in. (14 cm.)
1974.79 a, b

On each side Dutch ships in Capetown Harbor, with Dutch buildings, flags, and a later version of Table Mountain in the background. Predominantly mauve with iron red, blue, turquoise, sepia, black, and gold. Upper band of iron-red and black cell-diapers interrupted by reserves of stylized gold flowers.

In this scene the usual flat top of Table Mountain has been rounded (see cat. no. 1). The artist also confused the colors of the Dutch flag on the cover, painting it red, white, and red, instead of red, white, and blue.

Illustration of matching tea bowl and saucer in *Reeves Collection*,[16] pl. 1, no. 2.

4
PUNCH BOWL
European market, ca. 1785
Diam. 14¼ in. (36.5 cm.)
1974.92
See color plate I, page 10

Continuous depiction of the *hang* (ware-houses) in Guangzhou, with the flags of Prussia, France, Sweden, England, Holland, and Denmark. In foreground: Chinese and European merchants and Chinese vessels in the harbor; in background: pagodas, trees, and mountains. All in *famille rose* colors. At footrim: gold spearhead border; iron-red band with gold fret pattern. On interior rim: wide apple-green band with gold husks

edged by black and gold bands; gold fret pattern on iron-red band. Festoons of flowers connect alternating baskets of flowers suspended from ribbons and cartouches of gold scrollwork and purple network. Above each festoon, gold scrollwork on an iron-red ground and purple leaves. In center: an elaborate and varied leaf-and-floral border in *famille rose* colors and gold; apple-green banded medallion with gold darts edged by black and gold bands enclosing an iron-red vase of *famille rose* flowers.

Although the initials MT which appear on the Austrian Imperial flag stand for Maria Theresa, who died in 1780, the bowl itself was probably made

five years after that date. It was copied from a drawing made between 1770 and 1781, when the Austrian imperial flag flew in Guangzhou for two seasons as a front for a Hungarian-licensed French ship.[17]

The interior border of the bowl is based on Meissen borders of 1725–50, popular from 1775 to 1800 on China trade porcelain. A bowl with a similar basket border was brought home on the *Empress of China* by the ship's carpenter in 1785.[18]

Illustration of matching punch bowl in *Patterns*, pl. 49; and Crossman, fig. 36.

5
COVERED CREAMER, molded handle
   with heart
Probably English market, ca. 1785–90
H. 5½ in. (13.4 cm.)
1975.106 a, b

Under spout: a ship in iron red and black, heightened with gold, flying two partially drawn British flags and three red pennants. Green water with black wavy lines. Two floral sprays on either side. Upper mauve dart-and-dot border edged in iron red, with iron-red spearheads.

   The pear-shaped creamer, in use throughout the eighteenth century, is known with a variety of decorations.

This one was painted with a ship design by a porcelain decorator in Guangzhou, who left out the nationality of the flag, so that the sailor who purchased the creamer as a souvenir of his voyage could add his own. In this instance the sailor would have been British, just as the purchaser of a bowl in the Liebman collection depicting ships flying the Swedish flag (cat. no. 6) would have been Swedish.

6
BOWL
Swedish market, ca. 1785–90
Diam. 9⅛ in. (23 cm.)
1975.123

On two sides: a ship in black and iron red, heightened with gold, flying Swedish flags. Green water with black wavy lines. On other two sides and in center of interior: sprays of flowers. Iron-red double dot-and-pendant border on interior rim.

The poorly drawn Swedish flags were added to the ship at the request of the buyer. A flag of a different nation could have been substituted. A similar double-dot-and-pendant border appears on a saucer decorated with elephants, illustrated in *Reeves Collection*, fig. l6, cat. 42, and dated about 1790.

THE KILNS AT JINGDEZHEN

Unlike the port of Guangzhou, which became a town of porcelain enamelers and merchants in the eighteenth century, Jingdezhen, five-hundred miles inland, had been the site of the imperial kilns for more than one thousand years. It was at Jingdezhen that the Chinese developed a formula for hard-paste, or true, porcelain, as early as the Yuan dynasty (1279–1368), although they had manufactured porcelaneous stoneware centuries earlier.[19] The ingredients of Chinese porcelain are *kao-lin*, or China clay from the nearby mountainous region of *Gao-ling*, and *petuntse* ("little clay bricks"), both formed from the decomposition of granite or feldspar. To make porcelain, *kao-lin*, which is easily molded and fires white, must be combined in correct proportions with *petuntse*, a vitrifying agent that becomes transparent when fused. Firing at a high temperature of over 1250 degrees centigrade produces a hard, white-bodied ware that is nonporous, semi-opaque, and resonant when struck. At the peak of the China trade, thousands of factories and independent kilns supplied both imperial and Western requests for porcelain. The only Westerners to see the kilns, however, were a handful of Jesuits during the reign of the Kangxi emperor (1662–1722). The letters of Father d'Entrecolles, a Jesuit missionary who lived and taught at Jingdezhen, describe the process of porcelain manufacture there as an assembly-line method of mass production that depended upon an extensive division of labor. As many as seventy craftsmen might have worked on a single piece, each specializing in a different aspect of its production.[20]

In the early fourteenth century, the Chinese had begun to experiment with blue decoration on white porcelain. By painting a design on the unfired body of the ware in a pigment of cobalt oxide obtained from Persia, covering the design with a clear glaze, and firing at over 1250 degrees centigrade, they were able to fuse the glaze over the design at the same time that the body of the ware was vitrified. Blue and white porcelains were soon exported from China to the Near East and Europe,

their popularity reaching a peak in the seventeenth century. By 1720 there was a general decline in their manufacture as they became relegated to common, everyday tablewares in deference to the more colorful enamel services decorated in Guangzhou.

Despite the transfer of porcelain decoration to Guangzhou during the first quarter of the eighteenth century, Jingdezhen remained the manufacturing center because of its ideal location near the necessary natural ingredients. Once produced, undecorated wares were transported by boat to Guangzhou and decorated in expectation of European and, later, American orders. Porcelain decorators in Guangzhou used either a monochromatic grisaille or colorful *famille rose* palette of enamels in order to reproduce accurately the painted and engraved designs sent from Europe.

It was perhaps as a result of the ingenuity of the artisans at Jingdezhen that intricate underglaze-blue border patterns compatible with *famille rose* overglaze-enamel decoration that could be added later at Guangzhou came into fashion in the 1760s and 70s. The Gamon and Elphinstone services in the Liebman collection (cat. nos. 23 and 24), decorated with underglaze-blue borders of butterflies, frets, and hexagonal cell-diapers to which enameled coats of arms were later added in Guangzhou, are two such examples. Another underglaze pattern developed at Jingdezhen in the eighteenth century that remained popular well into the nineteenth on porcelains exported to America was known as Fitzhugh, in which four groups of flowers and emblems surround a central Chinese motif (see cat. no. 123). Compared to the techniques and subject matter of porcelain decoration for the Western market at Guangzhou, pieces decorated under the glaze at Jingdezhen were more Oriental in design. It was at Jingdezhen, however, not Guangzhou, that custom orders for the West in a full range of colors were filled, as were orders for porcelain decorated to suit imperial taste.

SHAPES OF EXPORT PORCELAIN

One of the most notable characteristics of Chinese export porcelain is that it is completely European in shape. The practice of supplying the Chinese with models of European tablewares to be copied in porcelain, begun by the Dutch in the 1630s, continued throughout the China trade. As ceramic, glass, and pewter samples were added to the original wooden models sent by the Dutch, drawings or engravings of the designs with which the porcelains were to be painted were also included. As illustrated by the Liebman collection, the majority of porcelains exported to Europe and America consisted of functional tablewares rather than decorative pieces, although vases and statuettes were exported on a smaller scale.

It is possible to trace the stylistic development of European tableware shapes through individual export pieces in the Liebman collection, as the shapes of Chinese exportware responded to changes in European fashion (fig. 4). In fact, the shapes of Chinese export

Fig. 4
Two sauce tureens: English creamware example on left (1975.161); Chinese export porcelain version on right (1975.152)

porcelain generally follow the evolution of contemporary European silver and ceramic shapes closely enough to offer guidelines for dating. Common in the middle of the century, but not in use after 1775, was a small teapot with a round bowl, straight spout, plain handle, and domed top. Like most Chinese export porcelain mass-produced at Jingdezhen, these teapots were sent undecorated to Guangzhou to be painted with Western designs. A diversity of subject matter appears on three

Fig. 5
Three teapots similar in shape with different designs: left, catalogue number 74; center, catalogue number 117; right, catalogue number 3

of them in the Liebman collection (see fig. 5). Like the teapot with a round bowl, an ovoid teapoy (cat. no. 91) was Oriental in shape, with no Western silver prototype.[21] It remained popular from about 1735 to 1770, when a square-shaped tea caddy with rounded shoulders derived from a European silver model came into fashion (fig. 6). Pear-shaped creamers, in use from the beginning of the eighteenth century (cat. nos. 5, 73, and 76), are derived from European silver shapes, just as a French silver or pewter ewer form, dating between 1700 and 1740, has been suggested as the prototype for a simplified helmet-shaped pitcher popular during the last quarter of the century (cat. no. 21).[22]

Not until about 1780 did a cylindrical teapot come into use (cat. no. 54). This shape is derived not from Oriental, but from contemporary English ceramic work, evidenced by the entwined strap handles and floral attachments which appear in Leeds creamware. The form of the lighthouse-shaped coffeepot (cat. no. 99), popular at the end of the eighteenth century, also comes from Leedsware.[23] It was common for saucers not to have an indentation for a cup. At the end of the century larger cups and saucers intended for breakfast use came into vogue, and by 1800 breakfast or coffee ''cans'' in the shape of small cylindrical mugs with straight, angular-sided saucers were popular (fig. 7). Spoon trays (cat. no. 111) and teapot stands remained popular until the close of the eighteenth century.

Fig. 6
Two tea caddies: left, catalogue number 91, ca. 1765; right, catalogue number 60, ca. 1795

Ordinary plates and soup plates gradually increased in size during the eighteenth century from approximately eight-and-one-half inches to nine-and-one-half inches. They were generally circular until about 1745, when an octagonal shape was introduced by cutting the circular plate to leave angular edges (cat. no. 15). By about 1760 the octagonal plate often had indented corners and a molded rim (cat. no. 89). Plates of a slightly later period with gadroon edges reflect contemporary silver prototypes (cat. no. 24). By the end of the century, the rim of a plate generally turned up. Large circular chargers or platters (cat. no. 10) were common until about 1755; after about 1770, oval platters (cat. no. 62) became fashionable. Whatever the shape of an individual plate, it would have been consistent with that of the entire service, just as teapots, creamers, and tea caddies from the same tea service would all have been similar in shape. Likewise, different services with pieces of similar shape were probably contemporaneous.

In order to appreciate the extensiveness of Chinese export services, it is helpful to refer to the records of the period, such as the notebook of an American trader from Rhode Island who was in Guangzhou in 1797.[24] We find, for example, that a breakfast service consisted of a teapot, milk jug (or creamer), sugar dish and stand, slop bowl, plate, and twelve cups and saucers. Additional pieces might have included a coffeepot, cake plate, butter boat, and stand.

Fig. 7
Coffee can and saucer (cat. no. 59)

An ordinary tea or coffee service differed from a breakfast set only in the addition of a tea caddy and usually contained forty-nine pieces. In a double tea set, there were approximately 101 pieces, including twelve cups with handles and twelve teabowls without, to be used at different times with the twelve saucers provided (fig. 8).

More extensive than tea or coffee services were dinner services, averaging 171 pieces. "The standard service was composed of plates and platters of a great variety of sizes, ranging from 6 to 18 inches, some specified as 'flat' and some 'deep'; soup, entree, salad, or dessert plates; vegetable, pudding, and pie dishes; salad bowls; soup and pickle tureens; sauce and butter boats; fruit dishes or baskets, all with stands; and salts."[25] Although punch bowls were not actually part of a dinner service, they were probably used before or after the evening meal and were ordered in large numbers, often as presentation pieces (cat. nos. 4 and 90).[26]

Fig. 8
Teabowl, saucer, and coffee cup (cat. no. 111)

ARMORIAL PORCELAIN

During the eighteenth century in England and on the Continent, royalty ordered Chinese export dinner services with their coats of arms. Catherine the Great of Russia (1729–96) had several services, one plate of which is in the Liebman collection (cat. no. 29). Families of aristocrats and wealthy merchants also ordered armorial porcelain. Although it cost close to ten times that of other available porcelain, it provided a novel way for affluent, heraldic families to display their arms. By the end of the eighteenth century there would have been few aristocratic families, country gentlemen, or wealthy merchants who did not own a Chinese armorial dinner service, or if they dined from silver, at least owned a Chinese armorial porcelain tea service, since the flavor of tea could be spoiled by silver.[27] For the English and continental markets from 1715 to 1805 six thousand armorial tea or dinner services were made, averaging two services per week.[28] Many families owned more than one armorial service, having ordered them over the years to commemorate special events such as an elevation in rank, the granting of arms, or a marriage. Two plates in the Liebman collection were made for the same client. Each bears the arms of Silveira impaling Tavora (cat. nos. 37 and 38) and was made about 1800. One is an elegant, unique design in gold and orange; the other is decorated with a common blue band with gold star border. Some wealthy merchants whose children married into the aristocracy ordered services with arms to which they were not rightfully entitled. In 1780 Richard Gamon, a commoner, ordered a service with arms that incorporated a ducal coronet (cat. no. 23), although his only link with the aristocracy was through his children. His children's marriages into the nobility did not make it appropriate for Gamon to imply by his coat of arms that he himself was a duke. Ironically, eight years after Gamon's death his eldest son, also Richard, was created a baronet.

In copying European arms onto porcelain, Chinese artists worked from bookplates and specially drawn and colored samples brought to Guangzhou by the supercargoes, who handled such special orders of armorial porcelain as part of their private trade.[29] Of the numerous services for English families with armorials copied from bookplates, one example, a teabowl for Drummond, is in the Liebman collection (cat. no. 13). The waiting time for a completely individualized service was close to two years from the client's order date. If the client chose instead to have his arms added in overglaze enamels to a stock border pattern available in Guangzhou, he could hope to receive the service on the supercargo's return voyage.

Fashions in English and Continental armorial styles evolved during the eighteenth century. In general, baroque shields, fashionable mainly from the 1740s to the 60s, are characterized by symmetry, balance, and lavish mantling (cat. no. 13). The asymmetrical rococo shields of the 1760s and 70s are smaller in proportion to the pieces on which they are displayed and lighter in appearance (cat. no. 21). Balanced neoclassical shields, popular from the 1780s to the 1800s, are often simple, spade- or oval-shaped, with minimal mantling (cat. no. 36).[30] Because heraldic fashion changed more rapidly in England than on the Continent, the arms on Portuguese services, for example, were often painted in a style that had been popular in England half a century earlier.[31] This is true of the arms on the Azevedo service (cat. no. 39), which are mid-eighteenth century in style, although the service dates as late as about 1805.

7
DEEP PLATE
English market, ca. 1724
Diam. 8⅞ in. (22.7 cm.)
1974.90

Central diamond-shaped shield with arms of Frederick with Marescoe in pretense and impaling Marescoe, surrounded by mantling of green and gold branches and iron-red, gold, blue, white, and puce scrolls. Inner gold rayonné border outlined in iron red. Gold and red cell-diaper band with chrysanthemums interrupted by four reserves, each containing possibly one of the *ba bao* (Eight Precious Objects). Chinese good-luck symbols of fish, pagodas, shells, and scrolls in red, green, gold, blue, and black. Outer stylized gold floral band

outlined in iron red. On reverse: a simple scroll border and four large chrysanthemums in iron red.

The diamond-shaped shield was commonly used by a widow to display her own arms impaled upon those of her husband. The repetition of the Marescoe arms, which appear both in pretense and impaled upon the Frederick coat, was not unknown for a woman who was also an heiress. Leonora Marescoe Frederick, for whom the service was ordered, was an heiress of Charles Marescoe of London. She probably ordered the service in 1724, four years after her husband's death, through her son, Sir John Frederick. A promoter of the South Sea Company, he was made a baronet in 1723 and ordered a service for himself the

following year.

The Frederick–Marescoe plate is the earliest example of Chinese armorial porcelain in the Liebman collection. The arms were carefully copied from a hand-colored original sent to Jingdezhen for that purpose. The red and gold Oriental decoration was the earliest pattern used for armorial porcelain and remained popular only until about 1725. Typically Oriental in its arrangement of borders and symbols, the design in no way interferes with the central armorial design. The iron-red and gold floral decoration on the reverse is comparatively unusual and not found on services decorated after about 1725.

Illustration of matching plate in Tudor-Craig, 16;[32] Howard, 202.

8
SOUP PLATE
English market, ca. 1735
Diam. 8⅞ in. (22.7 cm.)
1975.156

Central arms of Pryce impaling More with double crest, all above a banderole without motto. Gold spearhead inner border outlined in black. Four red-gold medallions with alternating crests of Pryce and More. Gold engrailed border at rim.

    This soup plate was probably both manufactured and decorated at Jingdezhen. The motto *VE DAL AM DARO* appears on a few pieces of this service, but not on the Liebman exam-

ple. The arms, which are not recorded, are Pryce of Gogirthen, and the impaled coat (on the right) is probably of More of Barnborough in Yorkshire and London or Coote. The service was probably made for Lewis Pryce, whose daughter Mary married John Campbell of Cawdor, a Lord of the Admiralty, in 1726. A later service resembling this one but enameled in Guangzhou is known.

    Illustration of matching plate in Howard, 42 and 411.

9
CHOCOLATE CUP, without handle, and
  SAUCER
Probably French market, ca. 1740
Cup: H. 3⅛ in. (7.9 cm.)
Saucer: Diam. 5½ in. (14 cm.).
1975.139 a, b
See color plate II, page II.

Central double coat of arms surmounted by coronet, probably of a French marquess, and supported by a lion and griffin, standing upon puce leafy scrolls entwined with blue and green garlands with an iron-red shell. Surrounding are a butterfly, floral bouquet, crane, and bouquet of grain and fruit. All finely painted in yellow, green, iron red, puce, mauve grisaille, and gold. Gold rim.

The cup is larger than any other in the Liebman collection and was prob-ably used for chocolate rather than tea. A shield identical to the one supported by the lion also appears on a service with iron-red decoration made about 1725 for the French market. The lack of a diaper border would suggest that this service is not earlier than the Qianlong period (1736–1795). The crane and butterfly have symbolic connotations in Oriental art; they are used here, however, as decorative motifs.

10
CHARGER
English market, ca. 1740
Diam. 12 3/4 in. (32.3 cm.)
1975.155

Central Oriental landscape with figures in soft shades of puce, blue, green, iron red, black, brown, and yellow. Undulating gold, iron-red, and green frame, surrounded by a vine of gold flowers outlined in black. Gold engrailed inner border outlined in iron red. Outer border with arms of Hudson (or Hodgson); three puce and gold floral sprays. Gold line edged in iron red at rim.

The original owner of this service was possibly Captain Robert Hudson, who was at Guangzhou on the *Loyal Blisse* in 1713 and again on the *Macclesfield* in 1721, 1724, and 1731; Captain Charles Hudson, who was at Guangzhou on the *Prince of Orange* in 1738; or Mr. J. Hodgson, who was supercargo on the *Prince of Wales*, at Guangzhou in 1736.

Compare the floral sprays on the outer border with those later copied in relief by the English Spode factory (fig. 2).

Illustration of matching charger in Howard, 336.

11
Pair of TEABOWLS, eggshell porcelain
English market, ca. 1745
Diam. 3 1/8 in. (7.7 cm.)
Diam. 3 1/4 in. (7.9 cm.)
1975.133 a,b

Arms of Woodward surmounted by crest and surrounded by leafy mantling, all in grisaille and gold. Grisaille and gold European scroll and lattice border with a panel of birds in a landscape on the back. Gold and black rim.

This border style is unique to services decorated in grisaille, although it also appears on services without arms. The coat of arms is that of Woodward of Hampton in Middlesex. It is not known for whom the service was ordered, or whether the merchant family of this name that lived in London during the eighteenth century is closely related.

Eggshell porcelain (*to tai*, "without a body") was made by placing a piece on the potter's wheel and paring it down until more than half the clay was removed. It was so thin that after glazing the porcelain seemed to consist only of glaze.

Illustration of matching teabowl in Howard, 349.

12
DEEP PLATE, valenced rim
Continental market, ca. 1745
Diam. 6½ in. (16.5 cm.)
1975.143

Central unidentified coat of arms. Green outer leaf-scroll border outlined in black; single lines of red and gold at rim.

This type of scroll-work border along with the greenish glaze appeared largely on services made for the Continent. This plate was possibly made for the Scandinavian market. By the 1750s it was less expensive to order European styles from Europe than from China. From this time on, armorial dinner services were not made exclusively in China, but also commissioned in Europe.

17
PUNCH BOWL
English market, ca. 1760
Diam. 14⅛ in. (36 cm.)
1974.64

On two sides: the arms of Howell surmounted by crest. On other two sides: a large floral bouquet in puce, mauve, iron red, blue, and green. Scattered floral sprays. On interior rim: gold spearhead border outlined in iron red. Large floral bouquet in center.

The arms and crest are probably of Howell.

Illustration of matching platter in Howard, 475.

18
DEEP PLATE, molded rim
Portuguese market, ca. 1760–65
Diam. 9⅝ in. (24.3 cm.)
1975.172

Central floral bouquet surrounded by looped floral garlands in lime green, pale turquoise, yellow, puce, mauve, and iron red. At top, crest of Diego José Vito de Meneses Coutinho, fifth Marquess de Marialva. Gold sawtooth border.

The style of the arms along with the molded rim and sawtooth border suggest a date of about 1760–65, when that border was popular.

Illustration from the same service in *Ceramica Branzonada*, vol. I, pl. III.[36]

19
SAUCER
English market, ca. 1765
Diam. 4 3/4 in. (12 cm.)
1975.127

Central arms of Younge surmounted by crest, and surrounded by mantling of scrolls and *famille rose* buds in puce, mauve, green, and blue. Wide underglaze-blue border with flowers and scrolls interrupted by four white reserves, each with an overglaze spray of gold flowers.

The arms are of Younge of Dorset. Possibly the service was made for Admiral Sir George Young, a relative of the Younge family, before he was granted arms. He served at Louisburg in 1758, as well as at Quebec, Havana, and later in India. The arms were added to the service in Guangzhou after it had already been decorated in underglaze blue at Jingdezhen.

Color illustration of matching saucer in Howard, opp. 144; also black-and-white photograph in Howard, 589; and matching service in Tudor-Craig, 98.

20
PLATE, molded rim
Portuguese market, ca. 1770
Diam. 9¼ in. (23.5 cm.)
1975. 126 a

Central arms of Antonio de Sousa Falcao de Saldanha Coutinho, surmounted
by coronet and surrounded by puce,
mauve, green, iron-red, and gold rocaille
mantling with floral festoons. Inner gold
spearhead border outlined in iron red.
Undulating leaf-scroll outer border with
flowers in puce, mauve, iron red, green,
sepia, and gold. Iron-red and gold rim.

Antonio de Sousa Falcao de
Saldanha Coutinho, for whom this ser-
vice was made, was a member of the
royal household.[37] This plate is one of a
pair in the Liebman collection.
Illustration of matching plate in
Ceramica Branzonada, vol. I, pl. XVII;
Mottahedeh, vol. 2, pl. 337.

21
Pair of HELMET-SHAPED PITCHERS,
  molded lotus leaves on lower body,
  detailed in iron red; handles with
  molded bamboo motif
English market, ca. 1778
H. 5 3/4 in. (14.5 cm.)
1975.189 a, b

Under spout: arms of Bowater with Duncombe in pretense. Shield edged with
gold and iron red, surmounted by a rain-
bow. Puce mantling and husk vine in
green. Floral festoons in puce, mauve,
green, and gold, suspended from gold
band. Scattered floral sprays on footrim,
along middle, and on lip.
    The service, for which several
Spode replacement pieces exist, was

made to commemorate the marriage of
John Bowater of Edgware to the honor-
able Frances Duncombe, eldest daughter and co-heir of Anthony Duncombe,
who was created Lord Feversham in
1747. The helmet shape, popular
throughout the eighteenth century, is
derived from a French silver or pewter
model.

22
TEABOWL and SAUCER
Dutch market, 1779
Teabowl: Diam. 3 1/8 in. (7.8 cm.)
Saucer: Diam. 5 in. (12.7 cm.)
1975.105 a, b

Central double coat of arms of Bal and Cats on mauve rocaille cartouches, surmounted by coronet and supported by a female figure in puce holding a green branch and a male figure in blue holding a bird. They stand upon a banderole inscribed S: BAL 1779 L: CATS above a gold scroll. Scattered floral sprays in puce, mauve, and green. Gold engrailed outer border with dot points. Gold rim.

The marriage commemorated by this service has not been traced. It was probably the Chinese artist who reversed the names on the banderole so that they do not match the arms.[38]

Illustrations from the same service in *Double Reflections*, pl. 53; Scheurleer, cat. 277.

23

COVERED SAUCEBOAT, lion-head
   handle, and UNDERPLATE
UNDERTRAY, molded and scalloped rim
English market, ca. 1780
Sauceboat with cover: H. 5 1/8 in. (13 cm.)
Underplate: L. 7 7/8 in. (18.7 cm.); W. 5 3/4
   in. (14.6 cm.)
Undertray: L. 10 3/8 in. (26.4 cm.); W. 8 1/8
   in. (20.4 cm.)
1975.175 a, b, c; 1975.176

Central spade-shaped shield with arms
of Gamon surmounted by a ducal coronet and crest, and surrounded by
mauve ribbon and floral mantling in
puce, blue, yellow, green, and iron red.
Inner gold bamboo and floral border in
puce, mauve, and green. Wide outer
underglaze-blue Fitzhugh border with
three rows of hexagonal diapers, butterflies, floral sprays, and dot-in-circle
edge.

   The covered sauceboat, matching
underplate, and matching undertray are

from a service ordered by Richard
Gamon of Hertfordshire, who died in
1787. His son, Richard, was created a
baronet in 1795. It is modeled after an
earlier service for Gamon, which was
similar except for the underglaze-blue
border. Compare this service to a contemporary one for Elphinstone (cat. no.
24).

   Illustration of matching plate in
Howard, 670; of earlier service in
Howard, 391.

24
PLATE, scalloped and molded rim
English market, ca. 1780
Diam. 9¾ in. (24.5 cm.)
1975.178 a

Central arms of Elphinstone surmounted by a baron's coronet and crest. Two savages with clubs as supporters stand upon banderole with motto *CAUSE CAUSIT*. Above them, a leafy mantling in puce, iron red, sepia, black, and gold. Inner gold and brown S-scroll border edged in black and gold. Underglaze-blue Fitzhugh border with three rows of hexagonal diapers, butterflies, diapers, floral sprays, and dot-in-circle edge.

One of a pair, this plate is from a service made either for Charles, tenth Lord Elphinstone, who died in 1781, or for his oldest son John (1737–1794), who succeeded as eleventh baron and was lieutenant governor of Edinburgh Castle. John's brother was a director of the East India Company, and the Elphinstone family owned three different services.

See the service for Gamon (cat. no. 23).

Illustration of matching platter in Howard, 973.

25

DINNER PLATE
English market, ca. 1780
Diam. 11¼ in. (28.5 cm.)
1975.100

Central medallion with crest of Hamilton and motto THROUGH enclosed by an apple-green band with gold husks edged in gold and black, surrounded by a gold scroll band. Scattered floral sprays in puce, mauve, brown, iron red, green, and gold alternating with gold and red floral sprays. Inner gold vine-scroll border. Green sawtooth edge; gold rim.

The Hamilton crest with motto on a framesaw was borne by the Hamiltons of Trebinshun. There were three possible owners of this service: Captain John Hamilton of the Royal Navy, who fought in the Battle of Quebec; Sir Alexander Hamilton, who owned eight ships at Guangzhou between 1780 and 1801; or another John Hamilton, captain of the *Bombay Castle*, which was at Guangzhou in 1796, 1708, and 1800.

Illustration of a matching reticulated basket and stand in Howard, 655.

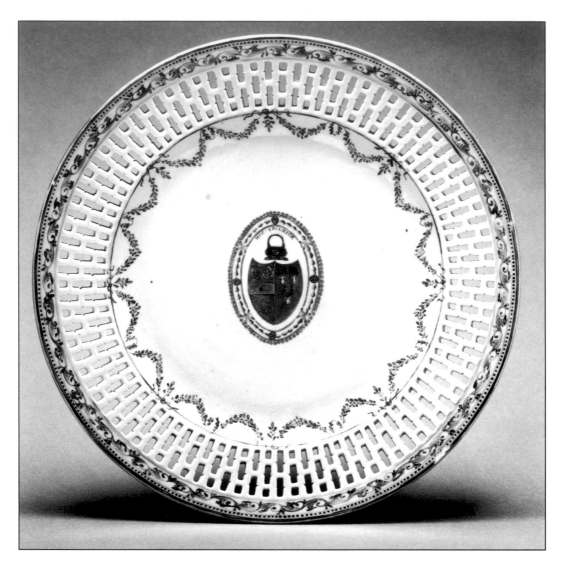

26
PLATE, reticulated border
English market, ca. 1780
Diam. 9½ in. (24.1 cm.)
1975.107

Central oval medallion with gold dots and puce husks interrupted alternately by blue crosses and black and gold oval medallions, enclosing a spade-shaped shield with arms of Grierson. Surmounting shield is crest and motto *HOC SECURIOR*. Inner border of floral festoons in puce, blue, iron red, and green. Outer foliate scroll border in mauve, puce, green, and gold. Bands of red dots enclosed by two gold lines, green band, gold rim.

The arms are of Grierson impaling possibly Anne of Yorkshire, Davyes, or

Hungford. The service was probably made for a younger brother or cousin of Sir Robert Grierson of Baldonell. The piercing on the plate probably derives from a long tradition of Chinese piercing adapted from Japanese porcelain, a technique later popular on German and English ceramics.[39]

See also catalogue numbers 28 and 29 for examples of pierced decoration.

Illustrations from same service in Phillips, pl. 49; and Howard, 637.

27
PLATE, notched octagonal rim
Scottish market, ca. 1780
Diam. 9⅛ in. (23 cm.)
1975.137

Central oval medallion surrounded by green and mauve dot-and-dart border and puce ribbon, enclosing a spade-shaped shield with arms of MacDonald, surmounted by crest and banderole with motto *PER MARE PER TERRAS*. Mantling of green leafy branches. Inner border of gold bamboo with buds in puce, mauve, and green. Floral festoons. Outer gold chain border outlined in iron red. Gold rim.

This service was probably made for William MacDonald (b. 1732) of Ranathan and St. Martin's Abbey in Perthshire. He was descended from a cadet branch of the MacDonalds, Lords of the Isles, who settled on Deeside after the Battle of Harlow in 1411. The combination of floral festoons with husk, chain, and bamboo borders has been described as "the last substantial decorative style on eighteenth-century armorial porcelain."[40]

Illustration from the same service in Howard, 622.

28
PLATE, reticulated border
English market, ca. 1785
Diam. 7½ in. (19 cm.)
1975.147

Central arms of Pakenham, Baron Longford, impaling Rowley, surmounted by coronet and supported by griffin and lion standing on gold leafy scrolls above a banderole with motto *GLORIA VIRTUTIS UMBRA*. Gold and green husk inner border; apple-green band with gold arches and lines at outer edge. Gold rim.

The service was probably ordered by Edward Michael Pakenham—a post captain in the navy and Member of Parliament for Longford, who succeeded his father as Baron Longford—and his wife, the former Catherine Rowley. Although they were married in 1765, the style of the service suggests a date of about 1785, when his mother was created Countess of Longford. The service must have been ordered before his death in 1792.

This service is similar in style to one ordered by Catherine the Great of Russia (cat. no. 29). The simplicity of design has been attributed to economic pressures.

Color illustration of matching plate in Howard, opp. 148 and 653.

Fig. 9. Reverse of plate with Chadwick arms.

33
PLATE
English market, 1791
Diam. 9¾ in. (24.7 cm.)
1975.103

Central spade-shaped shield with arms of Chadwick quartering Malvesyn, Carden, and Bagot, surmounted by a mauve ribbon and swags of gold husks. Mantling of crossed green branches. Inner blue dart-and-dot border outlined in gold. Wide outer blue spearhead-and-dot border connected by gold lambrequins; blue band edged in gold. On reverse: "Canton in China 24th Jan'y 1791." (See fig. 9.)

Although dates appear occasionally on armorial porcelain, this is the only known service dated in this man-

ner. It was probably ordered by Charles Chadwick, of Healy Hall, Ridware, New Hall, and Callow. His father was a lieutenant colonel in the Royal Lancashire Militia and a magistrate for the counties of Lancashire, Staffordshire, and Yorkshire.

Illustration of matching pieces in Howard, 741; Mudge, fig. 125a; and *Mottahedeh*, vol. 2, pl. 441. Reverse inscription also illustrated in Hyde, *Oriental Lowestoft*, pl. XIII;[47] Beurdeley, cat. 3; *Reeves Collection*, fig. 7; and Mudge, fig. 125b.

34
PLATE
English market, ca. 1795
Diam. 7½ in. (19 cm.)
1974.89

Central spade-shaped shield with arms of Hamond surmounted by coronet. Inner border of gold-leaf scrolls on blue band outlined in gold. Wide outer border of gold interlocking arches with blue and gold stylized flowers; gold stars on wavy blue band; gold crosshatching; gold leaves on blue band. Gold rim.

The arms on this service were granted to Sir Andrew, appointed lieutenant governor of Nova Scotia and created a baronet in 1783. Here, as on another service for Hamond about 1790, they are incorrectly drawn by the Chinese artist.

The border decoration matches that of another service in the Liebman collection with the monogram JVP (see cat. no. 59).

Illustration of another service for Hamond with a more elaborate border in Phillips, pl. 79; Howard 696.

35
PLATE, notched octagonal rim
American market, ca. 1795
Diam. 9½ in. (24.1 cm.)
1975.173

Central spade-shaped shield with arms of Morgan, surmounted by crest. Mantling of crossed green branches tied in gold. Inscription ELIAS MORGAN between shield and mantling. Gold chain inner border linked by blue dots. Wide outer border with dark blue arches on pale blue band with gold dots; gold dots on white band edged in gold; gold husks on blue band. Gold rim.

This service, made for Elias Morgan (1770–1813) of Clinton, Connecticut, is one of the few true armorial services made for the American market. It is unusual in showing Elias Morgan's full name under the coat of arms. He individualized the service by using his Welsh ancestors' coat of arms, while substituting a griffin for their traditional reindeer's-head crest.[48] The uncertain draftsmanship suggests that the Chinese artist copied a drawing rather than an engraving, which would have been more precise.

Illustration of matching plate in Howard, 747; Mudge, fig. 113.

36
SAUCER
English market, ca. 1800
Diam. 5½ in. (14 cm.)
1975.171

Central shield with arms of Fox surmounted by crest above a banderole with motto *FAIRE SANS DIRE*. Apricot and gold inner border with reverse sawtooth edge. Wide outer border of gold hatching on iron-red band; apricot band with brown interlocking leaves bordered on each side by gold stars; narrow blue band with gold dots. Gold rim.

The apricot border with S-scrolls and stars was popular between 1800 and 1805, and the style of the shield was also common during that period.

Another service for Fox is illustrated in Howard, 704.

37
PLATE, concave rim
Portuguese market, ca. 1800
Diam. 9¾ in. (24.9 cm.)
1974.91

Central arms of Silveira impaling Tavora with inscription *FINDIT QUASCUMQUAE* on Tavora coat, surmounted by crest and surrounded by mantling of green leafy branches. Gold interlaced inner border enclosing blue dots. Wide outer border of gold dots with crossed orange and gold ferns tied with gold ribbon. Gold band at rim.

This brilliant service was made to order for Bernardo José Maria de Lorena e Silveira, second Count of Sarzedas (1756–1818), Viceroy of Portuguese India during the late eighteenth century. The motif of crossed ferns derives from Western ceramic ornament.

Color illustration of a matching covered dish in Phillips, pl. 15; also pls. 81 and 82; Beurdeley, cat. 83.

38
PLATE
Portuguese market, ca. 1800
Diam. 7⅝ in. (19.4 cm.)
1975.148

Central medallion enclosing arms of Silveira impaling Tavora, surmounted by crest of Silveira and surrounded by motto *FINDIT QUASCUMQUE* and a floral garland in puce and green. Inner and outer blue-band border with gold stars and blue dots.

Like the preceding plate (cat. no. 37), this service was made for Bernardo José Maria de Lorena e Silveira, second Count of Sarzedas. Although roughly contemporary with it, this service lacks the lavish gold treatment of the other.

Illustrated in *Ceramica Branzonada*, vol. I, pl. III; *Mottahedeh*, vol. 2, pl. 381.

39
TEABOWL, SAUCER, and OVAL
   PLATTER, concave rim
Portuguese market, ca. 1805
Teabowl: Diam. 3½ in. (9 cm.)
Saucer: Diam. 6⅜ in. (16.1 cm.)
Platter: L. 10⅝ in. (27.1 cm.), W. 7¾
   in. (19.6 cm.)
1974.76 a, b; 1974.77

Central shield with arms of Antonio de Araugo de Azevedo surmounted by coronet and supported by a pair of putti in sepia, blue, and yellow. Pale green and gold leafy mantling. All on a black speckled ground. Blue banderole with AD. ARAUGO in gold. Inner border of blue diaper band with red dots. Outer border of boldly executed blue cartouches with alternating animals and Oriental landscapes in sepia.

Formerly in the McCann collection.

The "rubbed" patch where the arms were painted suggests that the service was shipped to Europe with borders only and the arms added there. The quality of the painting of the angel supporters varies considerably from piece to piece. The style of the armorial decoration predates the service by fifty years, but Portugal was slow to change heraldic styles.[49] Both the concave rims and border patterns indicate a date after about 1795. A similar dot-filled border appears on a plate with the Mysterious Urn (cat. no. 58).

Illustration of matching platter in Phillips, pl. 80; of vegetable tureen in *Mottahedeh*, vol. 2, pl. 382.

40
PLATE
Irish market, ca. 1810
Diam. 7⅞ in. (20.1 cm.)
1975.168

Inner gold band border with shell motif. Wide outer border of mauve ferns, scrolls, and gold leaves; blue, gold, and iron-red flaming cones; and green, mauve, and gold cone-shaped pendants. The border is interrupted at the top by McMahon crest and at the bottom by gold monogram DM.

The crest belongs to a branch of the McMahon family of County Clare, Ireland.

The design is an example of a European pattern adapted to Chinese export porcelain for the Irish and British markets after the East India Company ceased to import porcelain on its own account. The new intricacy of patterns at this time was perhaps made possible by the recent availability of painters who had previously been kept busy by East India Company orders.

Illustration of matching tureen in Howard, 790; and Beurdeley, cat. 112.

PSEUDO-ARMORIAL DEVICES

An equally attractive alternative to armorial decoration on Chinese export porcelain was a personal monogram. The variety of monogrammatic devices used ranged from elaborate pseudo-armorial mantlings, often with crests of ships, to simple medallions edged in gold, or even a floral spray in place of initials. Although the English and Europeans both selected armorial and pseudo-armorial decorations, it was unfashionable for Americans involved in the China trade to display their British arms in the aftermath of the American Revolution. Of the few identifiable armorial services for the American market, one made for Elias Morgan of Clinton, Connecticut is represented by a plate in the Liebman collection (cat. no. 35).

Americans preferred instead to have their monograms added to services already decorated with stock borders such as the Fitzhugh or blue band with gold stars, also popular in England. Limited to the American market, however, were porcelains painted with pseudo-armorial, patriotic devices. Two popular patterns that were armorial by implication only were the supporters and crest of New York State (cat. no. 55) and the American eagle (cat. nos. 63 and 64). Neither design had official status, but was produced by the Chinese for a popular American market. All of the New York State crests and supporters that appear on Chinese porcelain are painted according to the same color scheme, suggesting that the original design was probably drawn and painted in America and sent to Guangzhou as a model around 1785.[50] The American eagle, whose body was formed by a neoclassical, spade-shaped shield suitable for a personal monogram or floral spray, appeared in different versions, looking less like an eagle than what has been described as a sorry-looking sparrow.

Even when carefully painted, the popular patriotic designs for the American market do not approach in quality a fashionable monogrammatic device used in mid-eighteenth century Scandinavia and Holland. In these countries a service ordered to celebrate a marriage was often delicately painted with monograms superimposed upon a pair of rococo shields supported by two mythological figures of Neptune and Venus (cat. nos. 43 and 45). The owners of these services might have chosen to decorate them with their coats of arms, but preferred instead to use an intricate monogram.

It is surprising that a monogram also appears on a plate for the French market decorated with the Mysterious Urn in memory of Louis XVI and Marie Antoinette (cat. no. 58). The use of a personal monogram in conjunction with a political design kept secret among French royalist sympathizers is strange, for the owner would probably not have wanted to identify himself so soon after the French Revolution.

More direct is the full inscription *Peter Chapmam Parrott* above an altar of love on a mug in the Liebman collection (cat. no. 48). Treated in this way, the altar of love has become a pseudo-armorial device for Mr. Parrott, about whom nothing is known, despite the inscription of his full name. Chapmam is probably a transcription error by the artist for Chapman.

41
TEABOWL, eggshell porcelain
Probably Continental market, ca.
1740–60
Diam. 3 in. (7.6 cm.)
1975.134

Gold monogram JAC outlined in red; floral sprays in puce, iron red, and green. On interior rim: gold spearhead and engrailed border outlined in iron red; iron-red and gold bands.

This type of monogram, which can be read both frontwards and backwards, was especially popular in Scandinavia. It appears on other pieces in the Liebman collection (see cat. nos. 42 and 43).

42
COFFEEPOT, cornucopia spout,
   wishbone handle, berry finial, all with
   traces of gold
Continental market, ca. 1745
H. 9⅛ in. (23.2 cm.)
1975.191 a, b

On each side: a double marriage shield
with gold monogram JEBS inside an
elaborate shell, leaf, and floral cartouche. Peony spray below spout. On
neck: a border of strapwork, cartouches,
scales, and foliage. All in puce. Gold
spearhead, cup-and-ball border outlined
in iron red. Matching borders on cover.
   A similar border, derived from the
contemporary Viennese porcelain of the

Du Paquier factory, appears on two
plates in the Liebman collection decorated with religious subjects. The first is
decorated in grisaille with the Nativity
(cat. no. 108); the other, with the Crucifixion in bright colors (cat. no. 107).
   The shape of the coffeepot is
taken from a Meissen original of about
1740, although the finial on the lid is
Chinese.

43
DEEP PLATE
Danish market, ca. 1745
Diam. 9 1/8 in. (23 cm.)
1974.70
See color plate III, page 12

Central double marriage shield with gold monograms JC and CLM mounted on puce, gold, and blue shield-shaped cartouches. Neptune, with trident and fish, and Venus, draped in blue, support a coronet above the shields. They stand on a green ground with red and puce flowers. Wide border of four ochre, gold, and puce rocaille cartouches trailing green vines across an inner gold rosette border, and an outer pale green cell-diaper border outlined in puce. Gold rim.

The original engraving for this popular motif on Danish marriage ser-

vices is unknown. This shallow bowl is an earlier and more finely painted example than another pair of plates in the Liebman collection decorated with the same motif (see cat. no. 45). In its green cast, the body of this deep plate is similar to that of an unidentified armorial plate also made for the Scandinavian market (cat. no. 12). A similar rococo outer border appears on a service for the Swedish market with the arms of Grill, dated about 1745–55.[51]

Illustration of matching shallow bowl in Beurdeley, cat. 214.

44
COFFEEPOT, fluted body, double
    scroll-shaped handle with
    gold molded heart, dome-shaped
    cover
Swedish market, ca. 1750
H. 10½ in. (26.8 cm.)
1975.121

On each side: a double marriage shield
with gold monograms JARI and TAC on
cartouches of shells, scrolls, and festoons, surmounted by a coronet. Upper
border of angels pouring wealth, and
maidens with coronets, leaves, and
scrolls in grisaille and gold. Interspersed
among the figures, a fragmented banderole inscribed OGEN ICH ED HED
BESTANDIC. Matching border on cover.
Gold vine border at base of finial.

    If the fragmented inscription
OGEN ICH ED HED BESTANDIC is read
as *BESTANDIGHED OG ENIGHED*, it
translates from the Dutch as Steadfast-
ness and Unity. The Swedish *OG* has

been used, however, rather than the
Dutch *EN* for the word "and." Such a
combination of Dutch and Swedish
would not have been unusual, especially
if the service had been ordered by a
Dutch family through the Swedish East
India Company, or in celebration of a
marriage between a Swedish family and
a Dutch family living in Sweden.

    The shape of the coffeepot is dis-
tinctly Scandinavian, as are the indenta-
tions of the lip of the spout and the
double-scroll-shaped handle projecting
from the body. Examples of this type of
handle are known on teapots with
Swedish silver-gilt replacement spouts.

45
PLATE, molded edge
Danish market, ca. 1755
Diam. 8³/₄ in. (22.7 cm.)
1975.157 a

Central double marriage shield with gold reversible monograms AC and ME on a blue ground, mounted on puce and gold shield-shaped cartouches. Neptune, with trident and fish, and Venus, in blue drapery, support a coronet above the shields. They stand on a green ground with puce and blue flowers and two love birds in blue and red. Inner gold vine border outlined in black and iron red. Blue enamel and gold floral sprays; gold spearhead outer border, all outlined in iron red.

This is one of a pair of plates for-

merly in the McCann collection.

An earlier example of this motif can be seen in catalogue number 43. The border of floral sprays in blue and gold enamel can be compared with an earlier example of sprays in gold and mauve on a charger for Hudson (see cat. no. 10).

Illustration of matching plate in Phillips, pl. 41; of same monogrammatic device on a plate and coffeepot for the Dutch market, in *Mottahedeh*, vol. 2, pls. 396 and 397.

46
TEAPOT, molded scrolls on spout and
   handle; molded heart on
   handle
European market, ca. 1775–80
H. 5½ in. (13.8 cm.)
1975.187 a, b

Central medallion with monogram MM
and floral design in gold, surrounded by
apple-green band with gold darts edged
in gold and black. Gold and green dart
border; scattered floral sprays in puce,
blue, iron red, and green, suspended
from gold rings. Apple-green band with
gold husk upper border. Matching cover.
Gold sunburst on finial.

Another teapot in the Liebman
collection (not illustrated) was made
from the same mold but decorated with
an iron-red and gold landscape. The floral festoons and husk chains on this teapot were popular from 1775 to 1780, and
the green enamel band with gold husks
was also popular between 1775 and
1785.

47
TEABOWL, slightly scalloped rim, and
    SAUCER
English market, ca. 1775–80
Teabowl: Diam. 4³/₈ in. (11.1 cm.)
Saucer: Diam. 6¹/₈ in. (15.5 cm.)
1975.109 a, b

In center of saucer: spade-shaped shield with gold monogram JW surmounted by pseudo-crest of a ship flying the British flag above a black and gold torse. Mantling of crossed green leafy branches. Inner border of gold and green husks. Floral festoons in puce, mauve, green, iron red, and gold, alter-nating with gold ribboned and floral medallions in iron red and green. Gold saw-tooth outer border. Matching teabowl.

Similar pieces were exported to America, and only the British flag identi-fies this piece as having been made for the British market.

48
MUG, dragon-form handle in iron red
    and gold
English market, ca. 1780
H. 5 1/8 in. (13.1 cm.)
1974.62

On front: two figures, hands joined, before an altar of love in iron red, green, puce, mauve, yellow, grisaille, sepia, and gold. Inscription PETER CHAPMAM PARROTT. Wide border of cartouches with puce trelliswork, iron-red European landscapes, and floral sprays. Outer border of gold scrollwork.

The owner of this piece, Peter Chapman Parrott ('CHAPMAM' was probably an error by the artist), was perhaps a sailor. No reference to him has been found.

The border, which is similar to that on a deep plate decorated with chinoiserie (see cat. no. 79), is derived from Meissen porcelain.

As it appears on the mug, the altar of love is perhaps a late variation of the motifs associated with the Valentine pattern. It first appeared in England on Worcester porcelain around 1760 and was copied in China as late as 1778.[57] Here, instead of an altar with two flaming hearts impaled by Cupid's darts, a tree of golden apples, and a pair of lovebirds perched upon a bow and quiver, there is a tree sprouting from a heart with two lovebirds flying toward it, each carrying a branch in its beak. Combined with the owner's name above, the Valentine motifs have been incorporated into a finely painted pseudo-armorial device.

49
COFFEEPOT, entwined strap handle with
   blue floral attachments;
      cornucopia spout
European market, ca. 1780
H. 9⅛ in. (23.1 cm.)
1975.122 a, b

Spade-shaped shield with gold monogram TEB, surrounded by a mantling of
iron-red, gold, and mauve scrolls, floral
garlands, and blue husks with two
barely visible birds above. Under spout:
a gold and brown leather-bound book.
Scattered floral sprays. Underglaze-blue
dot-in-circle lower border. Upper gold
and sepia wavy band border edged in
black and gold. Underglaze-blue
Fitzhugh border with diapers, butterflies, and dots in circles. White
molded, scalloped bands. Matching
border on cover.

    This spout, derived from a Meis-
sen model dating to about 1735,

appears on an earlier coffeepot for the
Scandinavian market, dating to about
1750 (cat. no. 44). The moldings and
Fitzhugh border design on this coffeepot are similar to those on the contemporary Gamon and Elphinstone services
(cat. nos. 23 and 24). The style of the
shield, as well as its use in combination
with a gold and sepia wavy band and
blue Fitzhugh border, is similar to that
on an armorial service for Winter, made
about 1780. The significance of the book
under the spout, however, is unknown.

    Illustration of Winter service in
Howard, 680.

50
PLATE, notched octagonal rim
English market, ca. 1780
Diam. 9 in. (22.9 cm.)
1975.174

Central oval medallion with monogram WAS in iron red, black, and puce, surmounted by crest and surrounded by a mantling of leaves in iron red, gold, and grisaille, with sprays of flowers in mauve, iron red, blue, and green. Inner gold and iron-red dart border; floral festoons in puce, mauve, iron red, and green, with pendants in black, gold, and iron red. Outer black rope-twist border with red dots enclosed by chartreuse,

black, and gold banding.

Formerly in the collection of Mrs. Vincent Astor.

The monogram WAS, of which A stands for the surname and W and S for given names, has been previously read as A&R. Of the several families with a similar crest, the de Blois of Ireland possibly owned this service.

Illustration of matching teabowl in Howard, 970.

51
MINIATURE COVERED TEABOWL,
   eggshell porcelain, and SAUCER
Western market, ca. 1780
Saucer: Diam. 3³/₈ in. (8.6 cm.)
Teabowl: Diam. 2⁵/₈ in. (6.6 cm.)
1975.116 a, b, c

In center of saucer: a ship in black, iron red, sepia, and gold on pale green water with wavy mauve lines; inner gold husk border edged in iron red and interrupted by gold monogram SC on an oval-shaped shield surrounded by gold darts and green and gold ribbon. Floral festoons in puce, mauve, green, and gold suspended from a chartreuse dot border at rim enclosed by gold arches

with lines. Matching teabowl and cover, all finely painted.

   Similar covered teabowls were made as early as 1745 and produced well into the early nineteenth century for the American market. The small size of this service suggests not that it was a model but rather that it was intended for a child. The cover would have kept a beverage warm.

52
PLATE
English market, ca. 1780–90
Diam. 6³⁄₈ in. (16.2 cm.)
1975.142

Central oval shield with gold monogram WT outlined in iron red, surrounded by gold and mauve husk and floral mantling in puce, mauve, iron red, and green, surmounted by the crest of a British ship. Inner S-scroll border in gold and sepia. Gold rim.

This plate was probably decorated for a British sailor.

53
PUNCH BOWL
Continental market, probably Swedish,
   ca. 1785
Diam. 11⅝ in. (29.2 cm.)
1975.185

On two sides: a covered urn surmounted
by a cross with monogram FC or FJC on
urn cover and FL on urn body. On other
two sides: a floral bouquet. Feather festoons are suspended from a wide outer
border of solid bands, hatched lines,
and a center meander band. Band on
interior rim; bouquet in center. All
decorated in gold.

The decoration on this punch
bowl is similar to that on a slightly larger
one sold in London in June, 1964, with
the arms of Carpelan of Finland and the
names F. I. Carpelan and M. M. Carpelan. Both were probably imported by
the Swedish East India Company and
date to about 1785.

54
TEAPOT, entwined strap handle with
   gold floral attachments; gold
   strawberry finial and blue leaves on
   cover
Western market, ca. 1785–90
H. 5⅞ in. (15 cm.)
1974.84 a, b

On each side: a spade-shaped shield
with gold monogram ACL, surmounted
by crest. Above is an eye of God radiat-
ing rays in gold and iron red. Supporting
the shield are pale blue columns with
gold capitals and bases entwined with
gold rope. Leaf-scrolled mantling in
blue, gold, and puce; gold, blue, and
sepia Masonic symbols. Scattered floral
sprays in puce, iron red, and green.
Lower border of blue and gold darts.
Upper border of gold arches and lines
over an iron-red band; blue band with
gold stars. Matching borders on cover.
   The incorporation of a personal

monogram and unidentified crest into a
decorative scheme of Masonic elements
suggests that this piece was not officially
ordered by the Masons, but by a private
family with Masonic ties. Other pseudo-
armorial devices ordered by private per-
sons can be seen on a cup with the supporters and crest of New York State (cat.
no. 55), and on pieces with American
eagle decoration based upon the Great
Seal of the United States (cat. nos. 63
and 64).
   For another plate in the Liebman
collection with Masonic decoration, see
catalogue number 89.

55
COFFEE CUP
American market, ca. 1790
H. 2¾ in. (7 cm.)
1975.117

On front: a brown and gold shield with gold floral decoration surmounted by crest of New York State and supported by Liberty in blue and Justice in green. They stand on a banderole which bears no motto. Outer border of gold stars on a blue band edged in gold.

The earliest known engraving of the arms of New York State, dating from 1778, portrays Justice on the left and Liberty on the right, treading gently on a British crown. Both are in Dutch colonial costume.[53] The New York State arms had no official status; the Chinese used them commercially as a decorative motif for the American market. The presence of a gold floral spray instead of a personal monogram indicates that this cup is from one of the numerous services decorated with a stock pattern and exported in quantity between 1790 and 1810 for purchase by residents of New York State.

Illustration of other examples in Howard, *New-York*, 87 ff.; Mudge, fig. 103. Illustration of original engraving in Mudge, fig. 102.

56

SAUCER, slightly scalloped rim; on
  reverse in blue Arabic script:
  134
Indian market, ca. 1790
Diam. 6³⁄₈ in. (15.7 cm.)
1975.96

Central medallion consisting of a blue
band with white dots edged in gold, red,
and blue, enclosing a once visible gold
Arabic inscription NAWAB SIRAJ AL-
MUNA BAHADUR and date 1141 (1762)
surmounted by elephant crest. Mantling
of gold band with green leaves and
puce buds above a blue monogram
NSMB. Inner and outer borders of gold
stars on a blue band with gold arches
and spearheads.

 Nawab is a personal title. The
name Siraj Al-Muna means Lantern of
Hopes. Bahadur is not Arabic but probably an Urdu name.[54] The Arabic date of
1141, or the equivalent date of 1762, is at

least thirty years too early for the style
of the saucer. However, a service for the
Indian market inscribed with the name
and date of someone who died in 1747
but which was actually made thirty years
later for Middleton, an English family,
possibly as a commemorative service, is
illustrated in Howard, 663. It is therefore
possible that the Liebman saucer is also
part of a commemorative service made
thirty years after the inscribed date. The
significance of the numerals 134 in Arabic script on the reverse is unknown.

 For another plate in the Liebman
collection decorated with an elephant
motif, see catalogue number 88.

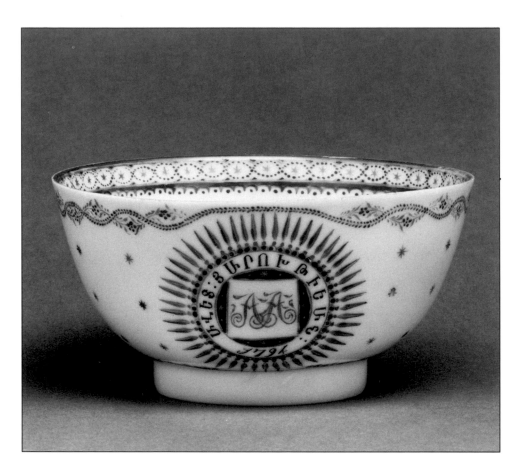

57
TEABOWL
Western market, 1794
Diam. 4³⁄₈ in. (11.1 cm.)
1975.153

On front: a gold monogram AA on a white square inscribed within a circular medallion of gold stars and dots on a blue ground. Surrounding is an Armenian inscription, the date 1794, and a sunburst design in blue and gold. Gold lower border of alternating gold and blue dots; widely spaced alternating gold and blue stars. Wide upper border of interlaced blue herringbone and gold leafy garlands with blue buds. On interior: a wide border of interlaced waves of blue dots enclosing gold stars, edged by a gold band with blue dots; blue arches with blue dots.

The Armenian inscription reads *AVET(IK) YAROKHT'IYAN*, and the English initials undoubtedly refer to the same person whose identity is unknown, but who was possibly involved in the China trade.

Illustration of a matching teabowl and saucer in *Mottahedeh*, vol. 2, pl. 484.

58
PLATE, concave rim
French market, ca. 1795
Diam. 9³/₄ in. (24.7 cm.)
1974.60

Central gold and black medallion with the Mysterious Urn in black, mauve, green, and sepia, revealing the profiles of Marie Antoinette and Louis XVI at the base of the urn, and the profiles of their children in the branches of the willow tree. Inner gold band border with hatched parallel lines and blue dots. Spade-shaped shield with gold monogram JJBS between inner and outer borders. Outer border of gold arches with blue dots and spearheads, gold band, and gold compartments with blue dots.

The Mysterious Urn design was taken from a print published by royalist sympathizers as a secret memorial to Louis XVI and Marie Antoinette after their deaths in 1793. It is unusual to find this design together with a pseudo-armorial shield and monogram, since the secrecy of the memorial is thereby belied. A pair of urns without a monogram was imported to Montreal for a former French royalist.[55]

Illustration of pieces with same subject without monogram in Phillips, pl. 90; *Reeves Collection*, fig. 31; *North America*, pl. 200. Illustration of print in Phillips, fig. 57.

59
OVAL PLATTER, orange peel surface,
  concave rim; COFFEE CAN and
  SAUCER
English market, ca. 1795
Platter: L. 13¼ in. (33.8 cm.), W. 10½
in. (26.7 cm.)
Coffee can: H. 2⅝ in. (6.8 cm.)
Saucer: Diam. 5⅛ in. (13.1 cm.)
1974.83; 1974.86 a, b

Platter, coffee can, and saucer with central blue and gold monogram JVP inside
an oval blue medallion edged in gold
with gold stars, surrounded by gold scallops and blue dots. Inner border of gold
leaf-scrolls on a blue band outlined in
gold. Wide outer border of gold interlocking arches with blue and gold stylized flowers; gold stars on a wavy blue
band; gold crosshatching; gold leaves
on a blue band. Gold rim.

Formerly in the McCann
collection.
  The orange-peel effect of the
glaze was intentional. Originally the
result of a firing mishap in which the
body and glaze reacted differently, the
irregular surface became popular during
the Ming period and was still imitated in
the eighteenth century.[56]
  Illustration of matching pieces in
Phillips, 217; *Oriental Lowestoft*, pl. XI.

64
TEAPOT, wishbone handle with gold
    dart-and-dot pattern; gold band on
    spout; gold finial
American market, ca. 1796–1805
H. 6 in. (14.8 cm.)
1975.181 a, b

On each side: a sepia and gold eagle
with drooping wings, sunburst, and gold
monogram JMC on a spade-shaped
shield. In its right talon, a laurel branch;
in its left, arrows of defense. On footrim:
gold chain border linked by a series of
blue dots. Upper border of blue dots
enclosed by gold arches and lines; interlaced blue dot and gold dot wavy lines
enclosing gold stars. Gold rim.

The shape of this teapot was copied from a silver model in both English
ceramics and Chinese export porcelain.
A silver example with a slightly thicker
lip, ball feet, and an 1812 hallmark is in

the Victoria and Albert Museum.[60] The
Spode shape book of 1820 includes an
example that is similar in over-all shape
to this teapot, except for a straight
spout.[61] It probably dates to about
1796–1805, at which time the gold chain
border with blue dots was popular. The
eagle here is similar to that on catalogue
number 63, except that the tips of the
wings are inverted.

Illustration of matching
lighthouse-shaped coffeepot with with
entwined strap handles in *Mottahedeh*,
vol. 2, pl. 513.

65
SAUCER, concave rim
American market, ca. 1825
Diam. 6¼ in. (15.8 cm.)
1975.144

Central asymmetrical shield with monogram CMJ, in sepia and gold, surmounted by eagle crest. Mantling of entwined gold scrolls and green branches. Gold-edged grape leaf border in mauve, brown, and sepia, with gold highlights.

The monogram CMJ is for Mary Walker Jones who married Thomas Ap Catesby in 1823.

Illustration of a matching soup plate in *North America*, pl. 346.

66
SAUCER
American market, ca. 1800–05
Diam. 6¼ in. (15.9 cm.)
1975.182

Central sepia and gold eagle with upturned wings and a gold and white striped spade-shaped shield with blue band across top. It carries the arrows of defense in its right talon and a laurel branch in its left. Inner gold and iron-red wavy border. Outer leaf-scroll border in gold and black on an apricot band edged in black and gold.

The leaf-scroll border on this pair of saucers is a variation of that on the saucer for Fox (cat. no. 36). Of those pieces in the Liebman collection decorated with the eagle from the Great Seal of the United States, this saucer is the most carefully painted. However, unlike the other examples, the eagle motif here has no monogram or floral spray on the shield which forms its body. In addition, the talons in which it carries the arrows of defense and laurel branch are reversed from the way they appear on the Great Seal.

67
PLATE, concave rim
American market, ca. 1810–20
Diam. 6¼ in. (15.8 cm.)
1975.115

Central sepia American eagle with drooping wings and spade-shaped shield on which the initial M is barely visible. In its beak, it holds a banderole with motto *E PLURIBUS UNUM*. In its left talon are the arrows of defense; in its right, a laurel branch. Surrounding is a Fitzhugh pattern with four sprays of chrysanthemums and peonies, each incorporating vases and scrolls. Outer border of diapers, frets, scales, and butterflies. All outlined in black and enameled in green.

Formerly in the McCann collection.

The owner of this service, whose initial M appears on the shield of the eagle, has not been identified. Several green Fitzhugh pieces from different services were in the McCann collection. This pattern was popular until about 1830, by which time the green enamel had become very thick and coarsely painted.

Color illustration of matching tureen with M clearly visible in Phillips, pl. 16; of matching plate in Mudge, figs. 90a and 90b.

68
PLATE, concave rim
American market, ca. 1820
Diam. 7⅞ in. (19.9 cm.)
1975.124

Central medallion with monogram GHM, surrounded by motto *PROSPICERE QUAM ULCISCI* and surmounted by a crest. Fitzhugh pattern with four sprays of chrysanthemums and peonies, each incorporating vases and scrolls. Inner border of three rows of hexagonal diapers. Outer border with diapers, frets, scales, and butterflies and dot-in-circle rim. All in underglaze brown and sepia.

This service, which was made for Gabriel Henry Manigault of Charleston, South Carolina (1788–1874), was possibly ordered through his brother Charles Izard Manigault (1795–1834), who sailed to China on December 19, 1821. Several pieces from this service are in the col-

lection of the Museum of Early Southern Decorative Arts, Winston-Salem, North Carolina. Although the service bears the Manigault crest and motto. it is not a true armorial service, as is a service for Charles Izard with a full coat of arms taken from a bookplate Izard had designed and engraved in Australia.[62] Companion portraits of the parents of Gabriel Henry and Charles Izard Manigault, painted by Gilbert Stuart in 1794, are in the Albright-Knox Art Gallery, Buffalo, New York.

Color illustration of a matching coffee can in *Reeves Collection*, pl. III, no. 4; and in *North America*, pl. 367.

WESTERN DESIGNS AND TECHNIQUES

European painting, enameled watchcases, and Limoges enamel bowls brought to China at the end of the seventeenth century fascinated the Chinese. Under the Kangxi emperor (1662–1722), the Chinese enlisted the help of Jesuit artists at the imperial court in teaching them to enamel on copper in imitation of Western enamels and oils, a technique the Chinese later applied later to porcelain. A letter from a Jesuit missionary in China written in 1720 describes the "very rapid progress" of the Chinese in mastering the technique of enameling after a period of only five or six years.[63] One bowl in the Liebman collection (cat. no. 16) is from a large service for Saldanha de Albuquerque of Portugal that has porcelain platters and matching copper covers thought to have been enameled by the same artisans in the same shop.[64]

To the familiar Chinese overglaze enamel colors of green, yellow, blue, and black, a new palette of European enamels was added. Known as *famille rose*, it enabled Chinese craftsmen to imitate the reds, pinks, and purples found in Western paintings. Unlike the underglaze colors that were fired to over 1250 degrees centigrade at the same time as the porcelain, the new overglaze enamels were added to an already fired piece and reheated in a muffle kiln just hot enough to fuse them. From Europe also came a white enamel derived from tin, which the Chinese began to mix with other colors to produce the shaded effect of Western oils and watercolors.

Taught by the Jesuits, the Chinese were also quick to adapt Western engraving techniques to porcelain by painting it with precise, cross-hatched lines in a black ink that would not fade in the kiln. By 1730 they had perfected a monochromatic palette known as grisaille that enjoyed a decade of popularity for both armorial and biblical subject matter copied onto Chinese export porcelain (see cat. nos. 11 and 104).

At that time and possibly as early as 1715, enamel and probably grisaille decoration was moved from Jingdezhen to Guangzhou.[65] It was there that the various East India companies brought such European art forms as enameled watchcases, coins, ceramics, and prints after popular European paintings and topical political subjects, and engravings of biblical and mythological scenes, to be copied. Often it is possible to identify the original for a design on Chinese exportware, such as a Rubens painting, although the particular art form on which it reached China and from which it was copied remains obscure. Many of the allegorical and mythological subjects after Italian originals probably reached Guangzhou on Italian majolica or enamel watchcases. Biblical subjects, however, appeared on English and Delft pottery, engravings, textiles, and silver.

Whether from the Bible, classical mythology, or contemporary European politics (see cat. nos. 58 and 77), the scenes copied onto Chinese export porcelain from samples provided by the East India companies mirror eighteenth century European taste and fashion. While at Guangzhou, the East India men also encountered designs commissioned elsewhere in Europe, many of which they also brought home. Guangzhou has therefore been described as "a clearing house not only for an exchange of styles between East and West, but between segments of European culture itself."[66]

Fig. 10. Reverse of Rotterdam plate.

69

PLATE, valenced rim. On reverse:
    Chenghua mark within double ring
Dutch market, ca. 1690–95
Diam. 7⁷⁄₈ in. (20.3 cm.)
1975.151

Central scene depicting the pillage of Chief Bailiff Jacob van Zuyle de Nyevelt's house during the Rotterdam riots of 1690. Outer diaper border interrupted by four reserves, two of which contain flowers, and two, symbols from the *ba boa*, or Eight Precious Objects. On underside of rim: a continuous curvilinear band with flowers and swastikas. All in underglaze blue.

This is the first appearance of a contemporary political scene on Chinese export porcelain. It was copied from a commemorative medal by Jan Smeltzing, struck in pewter, gold, and silver despite a 1688 Dutch edict that prohibited the making, printing, and retailing of "scandalous and infamous lampoons."[67] The Smeltzing medal was secretly sent to China as a model for a large porcelain order, of which over fifteen plates besides sets of cups and saucers are known today. Like the other examples, the Liebman plate is awkward in style, since the Chinese artists had varying degrees of difficulty in copying this crowded scene. Many of the plates have Chinese reign marks on the back. The mark of the Ming Dynasty Emperor Chenghua (1465–87), which appears on the Liebman plate, was commonly used at the end of the seventeenth century, as were symbolic marks, because an edict of 1677 forbade the use of the mark of the ruling Kangxi emperor (1662–1722).

Compare this plate with two others in the Liebman collection that also have political overtones (cat. nos. 58 and 77).

Illustrations of plates with same scene in *Patterns*, pl. 12; Garner, *Oriental Blue and White*, pl. 68;[68] Beurdeley, cat. 170; and Scheuleer, cat. 132; of cup and plate in *Mottahedeh*, vol. 1, pl. 15.

70

SHALLOW BOWL, valenced rim, molded
  edge, molded exterior body. On
  reverse: Kangxi mark within double
  ring
French market, ca. 1700–10
Diam. 13 1/2 in. (34.5 cm.)
1975.113

Central scene with a lady seated at a
table, a gentleman standing, and a girl
carrying flowers, followed by a little boy,
possibly a servant. The lady and girl
wear their hair in a style made popular
by the Duchesse de Fontanges, mistress
of Louis XVI. In background: a pagoda

and tree. Wide border of lotus-shaped
panels depicting pairs of Chinese
women amidst flowers and rocks. The
panels are separated by swastika diapers. On underside of rim: three flowers
with branches. All in underglaze blue.

  Formerly in the Mottahedeh
collection.

  The subject is after an unidentified French print. Because it is similar in
style to a print of *The Music Party*
engraved by the Parisian Nicolas Bonnart (1646–1718) and drawn by his
brother Robert, it has been suggested
that this scene also derives from a print
by the Bonnart brothers, possibly illus-

trating the sense of smell.[69] It is the
finest example of blue and white decoration in the Liebman collection. Charac-
teristic of underglaze-blue decoration
painted between 1695 and 1730, the
light and shaded areas of blue were
achieved by the amount of cobalt the
artist applied with his brush, not by his
use of shaded hatched lines. The use of
the Kangxi mark on the reverse is rare in
light of the edict of 1677 forbidding the
use of the mark of the ruling emperor.

  Illustration of similar shallow bowl
in Beurdeley, fig. 12, *Mottahedeh*, vol. 1,
pl. 36.

71
DEEP PLATE, valanced rim. On reverse:
  ai ye mark within double ring
French market, ca. 1710–20
Diam. 6⅛ in. (15.5 cm.)
1975.112

Central scene of a family group similar to catalogue number 70, possibly after the Bonnart brothers. On underside of rim: three flowers with branches. All in underglaze blue.

This small plate is a less finely rendered version of the same scene as the previous entry. The *ai ye* (artemisia leaf) mark appearing on the reverse is a symbol of good omen used during the Kangxi period. At that time it was forbidden at Jingdezhen to use the seal or characters of the emperor's reign mark on porcelain, so that the emperor's name would not be defiled if the piece were to break. Symbols and reign marks on export porcelain do not necessarily refer to the period of a piece's manufacture; some, such as catalogue number 69, imitate those of an earlier period. For this reason the quality of the potting and decoration are more reliable guides for dating than the marks themselves.[70]

72
PLATE
Continental market, ca. 1725
Diam. 9¼ in. (23.4 cm.)
1974.87

Central scene of a couple walking with a greyhound in an Oriental landscape with a fence. All in iron red, gold, black, and pale green. Gold inner border edged in underglaze blue. Wide border of buds, flowers quartered by the attributes of the Eight Immortals, cell-diapers in iron red, black, sepia, and gold highlights over buds, leaves, and an outer band in underglaze blue. On underside of rim: two branches in underglaze blue with iron-red buds.

A pale green has been added to the traditional Chinese Imari palette of iron red, gold, and underglaze blue as seen in the contemporary plate for

Lenora Marescoe Frederick (cat. no. 7). This scene, although sometimes called Governor Duff and his Wife, probably represents a "happy Frisian couple" of Dutch tradition.[71] The border, however, is unlike others known for the Dutch market.

A small bowl with the same subject matter in iron red, grisaille, and gold is also in the Liebman collection (not illustrated).

Color illustration of matching plate in Scheurleer, *L'Armoire hollandaise aux porcelaines de Chine*, pl. 49;[72] *Mottahedeh*, vol. 1, pl. 127; Beurdeley, cat. 192.

73
CREAMER
Continental market, possibly Dutch, ca.
   1735–40
H. 3⅞ in. (9.9 cm.)
1975.118

Continuous scene with workman, burros, carts, horses, and a rugged shoreline. All in grisaille, brown, and gold. Scroll border in grisaille and gold.

The original for this scene, possibly a European ceramic model, has not been identified. The scene has been called the Building of the Zuider Zee Dam, as well as Road Along a Rugged Shore. The tight overlapping scroll border is copied from Hausmalerei on Meissen porcelain. Hausmalerei literally means "home paintings" and is a type of painted decoration found on German porcelain. Early in the eighteenth century, the large factories such as Meissen sold undecorated wares, usually seconds, which were then painted by individual painters or workshops unrelated to the factory. As the quality of the painting declined after mid-century, the factories stopped the release of undecorated porcelain.[73]

Illustration of same scene with a different border in Phillips, pl. 65.

74
TEAPOT
European market, ca. 1740
H. 5½ in. (14 cm.)
1975.95 a, b

On each side: a pair of Eastern musicians. One, dressed in pale yellow, blows a horn; the other, dressed in pale blue, blows a bugle from which hangs a yellow banner. They stand on an underglaze pale turquoise ground. The rest of the teapot is in black enamel. Gold spearhead border at base. Upper border of gold spearheads, gold diamonds on black ground, and black diamonds on gold band. Gold diamonds at handle and at spout attachments.

The shape of this teapot as well as the spearhead border were already in use about 1740, when decorations on a glossy black enamel background became popular. The brownish-black pigment used here

has the same composition as that used for black outlines. Green enamel has been applied over it.[74] It has been suggested that the design was by Cornelis Pronk, a designer employed by the Dutch East India Company. The even spacing and regularity of design show that the pattern originated in Western Europe, "where it was sold as yet another product of the 'mysterious East.'"[75] This pattern was repeated over a number of years, and examples of it are in New York in The Metropolitan Museum of Art.

Illustration of a matching teapot in Scheurleer, cat. 92; of bowl with different border in *Mottahedeh*, vol. 1, pl. 299.

75
PLATE
Continental market, ca. 1740
Diam. 9⅛ in. (23.2 cm.)
1975.108

European landscape with men drinking on a river bank in shades of green, yellow, iron red, puce, mauve, blue, sepia, grisaille, and gold. Inner gold C-scroll border with buds and hatching in grisaille. Outer stylized border of scrolls, leaves, and flowers in iron red, sepia, green, grisaille, and gold.

In its tight, heavy scrollwork, the border on this plate resembles that of the Liebman creamer (cat. no. 73) and is derived from German Hausmalerei. The scene, too, possibly derives from a fictitious Hausmaler scene after Meissen porcelain decoration. Unlike the usual drinking scenes, in which peasants are portrayed, here gentlemen are shown.

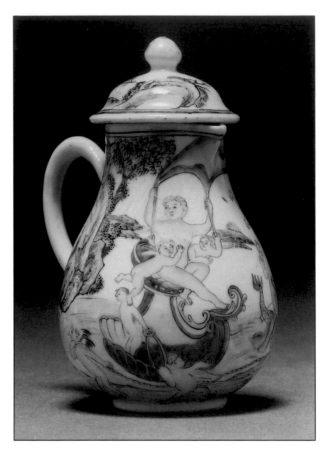

76
CREAMER
Continental market, ca. 1740
H. (without cover) 3¾ in. (9.5 cm.)
1975.114 a, b

Continuous scene representing *Water* after Francesco Albani, with Venus, putti, sea nymphs, and gods. All in brilliant puce, brown, yellow, shades of blue and green, gold, and black. Gold line edged in black on rim.

The composition is taken from an engraving of *Water* by Antoine Herisset (1685–1769) after four paintings representing the elements by Francesco Albani (1578–1669) in the Borghese Palace.[76] All of the paintings were depicted on Chinese export porcelain. Herisset

simplified the original composition by eliminating several figures, and the Chinese artist simplified it even further. This popular subject was painted over a period of time with various borders, but the Liebman example probably dates to about 1740.

Illustration of the entire series on export porcelain in Williamson, *The Book of Famille Rose*, pl. XXXIX,[77] and Palmer, *A Winterthur Guide to Chinese Export Porcelain*, pl. 7.[78]

77
PLATE
Scottish market, ca. 1740–45
Diam. 9 1/8 in. (23.2 cm.)
1974.65
See color plate IV, page 13

Central scene of two Scottish Highlanders in kilts. One carries a musket and sword; the other plays a bagpipe. All in iron red, black, yellow, gold, sepia, puce, blue, and turquoise. They stand upon a chartreuse, turquoise, and black ground. Inner gold-line border outlined in iron red. Four grisaille border panels with gold and iron red, two of which depict a flowering branch with a red-breasted bird; and two, an Oriental landscape with figures and a mountain. Gold line outer border.

The design is a composite of two engravings by George Bickham (1684?-1769) done about 1743.[79] Both figures were Jacobite martyrs. Piper Macdonnel, on the right, is said to have been piper to Prince Charles. He was sent as a convict to Georgia.[80] The figure on the left is probably one of three privates of the Highland Regiment shot in the Tower for deserting the Stuart cause. The latter design appeared as the frontispiece to *A Short History of the Highland Regiment*, engraved and published by the artist in 1743.[81] The same prints were also sold separately as a set the same year by John Bowles at the "Black Horse" in Cornhill and taken to China, evidently, where they were carefully copied. The twenty known plates with this design show no signs of wear, suggesting that possibly they were put away, as the mutiny and martyrdom of the Jacobites were forgotten by the time they were delivered in about 1745.[82]

The border panels of alternating Chinese landscapes and birds were copied from Meissen examples of about 1725–35. They appear on other pieces in the Liebman collection (see cat. nos. 79 and 81). Chinese artists copied Meissen chinoiseries probably without realizing that they were, in fact, copying Western renderings of Oriental figures and designs.

Color illustrations of matching plate in Beurdeley, pl. XIX; *Patterns*, pl. 38; and Scheurleer, cat. 205.

78
COVERED CREAMER
Continental market, possibly Dutch, ca.
  1745
H. 5 1/8 in. (13 cm.)
1975.146 a, b

An amorous couple in Dutch costume departing for the Isle of Cythera, with Bacchus leading the way. As they walk, the man pours wine into a shell held by the woman. Beyond is a Chinese landscape. All in black, heightened with gold and iron red. Oriental landscape on cover.

The scene is after a 1708 engraving *Pélérins de l'Isle de Cythère* by Bernard Picart (1673–1733), a Frenchman active in Amsterdam.[83] The subject, which is based on a ballet or opera popular in Paris at the beginning of the eigh-

teenth century, also inspired Watteau's painting *L'Embarquement pour Cythère*. It is possible that the print was sent to China because of its popularity on Meissen porcelain between 1730 and 1735.

For another design thought to be after a Picart engraving, see catalogue number 87.

Illustration of plate with different border, in Phillips, pl. 55; Beurdeley, cat. 122; Williamson, pl. XIV; cover of *Antiques* 15 (June 1929); and *Mottahedeh*, vol. 2, pl. 354.

79
DEEP PLATE
Continental market, possibly Dutch, ca.
  1745
Diam. 8¾ in. (22.4 cm.)
1975.169

Central dark brown and gold cartouche surrounded by iron-red, gold, and puce feather scrolls and red trelliswork enclosing a harbor scene with figures and landscape in pale turquoise, green, mauve, puce, iron red, yellow, blue, sepia, and grisaille. Inner gold spear-head border outlined in iron red. Four border panels, two of which depict a bird on a branch in puce and two, mountainous Oriental landscapes in grisaille. Gold line at rim.

Both the central cartouche with a harbor scene and the shapes of the border panels are derived from Meissen originals that possibly reached China through the Dutch East India Company, since there was no direct trade between Prussia and Guangzhou.[84] Once the Meissen patterns became standard on Chinese export porcelain, they were shipped from Guangzhou to several European countries in direct competition with patterns produced by European factories.

For another plate with a design derived from Meissen, see catalogue number 80.

Illustration of matching tureen and platter in Phillips, pl. 64; Beurdeley, cat. 78.

Fig. 11
**SAUCER, Meissen hard-paste porcelain.
On reverse: crossed-swords mark in gold,
within three concentric iron-red rings, ca.
1725–30
Diam. 5⅝ in. (14.2 cm.)
1975.130**

Central harbor scene with mauve lustre and gold curving cartouches, surrounded by iron-red and purple arabesques; wide outer gold-lacework border. Harbor scenes inspired by contemporary European engravings were painted on Meissen porcelain by J. G. Herold and C. F. Herold, who both created their own chinoiseries. These harbor scenes, together with a curved central cartouche, decorative arabesques, scrolls, and lacework border were copied by Chinese artists on export porcelain until the middle of the eighteenth century. It was at Meissen in 1708 that Johann Friedrich Boettger discovered the secret formula for manufacturing true porcelain.

80
PLATE
Continental market, ca. 1745–50
Diam. 9 in. (22.9 cm.)
1975.190

Central brown and gold cartouche enclosing a Western landscape with figures jousting, surrounded by feather scrolls and trelliswork. All in iron red, puce, blue, shades of green, sepia, grisaille, brown, and gold. Gold inner spearhead border edged in iron red. Wide border of blue leaves and dots,

gold scallops, and red and puce feather scrolls.

As on the deep plate (cat. no. 79), the central scene and borders are derived from Meissen.

Illustration of matching plate in Beurdeley, fig. 79.

81
PLATE
Western market, ca. 1750
Diam. 9⅛ in. (23.2 cm.)
1974.66

Central scene with Don Quixote in blue armor with a puce mantle, holding a gold lance, astride a dappled brown horse led by Sancho Panza dressed in pale green, iron red, blue, and black. Two women in blue, apricot, and puce peer from behind a tree with yellow and green foliage. The Oriental landscape is sketched in grisaille and pale green, with clumps of green and yellow grass. Gold line inner border. Four grisaille border panels, two of which depict flowers and a bird; and two, an Oriental landscape.

Gold line outer border.

The scene is taken from an engraving published in 1746 by Bernard Picart (1673–1733) after a painting by Charles-Antoine Coypel (1694–1752) that did not include the two women. An earlier version on Chinese export porcelain (done about 1742) was faithfully copied from an engraving of about 1741 by J. Folkema (1692–1767), also after the Picart engraving. The design on this plate has been adapted from the earlier engraved and porcelain versions.[85]

82

MINIATURE TEABOWL and SAUCER
European market, ca. 1750
Teabowl: Diam. 1¾ in. (4.3 cm.)
Saucer: Diam. 2¾ in. (7.1 cm.)
1975.166 a, b

Central scene of a woman beckoning to three children in a garden, in black and iron red with gold highlights. Gold engrailed border with ball points outlined in black.

This tiny teabowl and saucer were probably part of a tea service made for a doll's house. There are two well-known doll houses in England. One, at Nostell Priory in Yorkshire, has furniture by Chippendale. The other, at Uppark in Hampshire, has hallmarked silver of about 1720. Both houses have Chinese export porcelain services. A covered miniature teabowl and saucer in the Liebman collection (cat. no. 51) were probably also made for a child. A depiction of children appears as well on two miniature coffee cups in the Liebman collection (cat. no. 96).

83
SAUCER
Possibly Continental market, ca. 1750
Diam. 4¾ in. (12.1 cm.)
1975.111

Central scene of the Eyes of Brother Philip, all in black with flesh tones. Black rim with gold.

The scene is taken from a fable by La Fontaine, "Les Oies du Frère Philippe," that also inspired a painting by Nicolas Lancret from which the engraving for this saucer was copied. A widower, Filippo Balducci, who lived with his son in a cave on Mount Asinaio, took him to Florence for the first time at the age of eighteen. When the son saw pretty young women for the first time

and asked his father what they were called, his father replied that they were goslings and to be avoided. The son desired them nonetheless.[86] The scene is known both in grisaille and in *famille rose* enamels, with and without borders. A matching creamer is in the Liebman collection.

Illustration of plate with border of floral sprays in Scheurleer, cat. 218; with garland border in *Mottahedeh*, vol. 1, 345.

84
BOWL
Continental market, ca. 1750
Diam. 4³/₄ in. (12.3 cm.)
1975.102

On front, a gold-edged medallion with scene of a lady at her toilet. To her left, a servant pours water into a tub. All in black, with flesh tones. On back: a bouquet of peonies in black. Gold engrailed inner border with ball points outlined in black. Black flower in center of interior.

The subject of a lady at her toilet was a popular one, and other later examples are known. The engrailed border was also popular on armorial services of this period. It appears as well on a doll-sized teabowl and saucer in the Liebman collection (cat. no. 82).

85
PLATE
Dutch market, ca. 1750
Diam. 9⅛ in. (23 cm.)
1974.73
See color plate V, page 14

Central scene of the Bull's Cruelty or Wonder at Zaandam, in which a farmer's wife, tossed into the air by a bull, gives birth prematurely to a child while the bull mortally wounds her husband. A boy flying the kite which had frightened the bull is on the right. Dutch landscape in background. All in green, brown, blue, iron red, puce, mauve, white, and black. Gold spearhead border edged in iron red. Gold rim.

This subject is known on both Dutch ceramics and Chinese export porcelain. The event is said to have occurred in 1647, and this design was probably taken from a print made one hundred years later to commemorate the family's unusual death.[87]

Illustration of teabowl and saucer with same subject matter but without a border in Beurdeley, fig. 66; of plate in Scheurleer, cat. 358; and of bowl in Palmer, fig. 12a.

86
PLATE
Probably Dutch market, ca. 1750
Diam. 9¼ in. (23.5 cm.)
1974.67

Central scene of boy fishing. Border of cartouches with scalework, quilting, and peacocks interwoven with floral garlands. All in puce, except for inner border and rim of gold lines edged in grisaille.

The scene is taken from a design by Abraham Blocmaert (1564–1651), included in his notebook and later engraved, possibly by his son Cornelis II (ca. 1603–80).[88] An engraving of the same scene as on the plate was published by C. J. Visscher.[89] The scene, known with various borders, was also painted in grisaille. The border of this plate is similar to that on other pieces in the Liebman collection decorated with Juno and the Peacock (see cat. no. 111).

From about 1735 to 1755, coffee and tea services and plates, rather than full dinner services, were decorated with idyllic scenes like this one. They were probably displayed in cabinets rather than used, as suggested by their fine condition.

Illustration of matching plate in Beurdeley, cat. 123; and *Mottahedeh*, vol. 2, pl. 362.

87
PLATE
Continental market, possibly Dutch, ca.
    1750–60
Diam. 8⅞ in. (22.6 cm.)
1975.149

Central scene of the Embroideress, with heavy drapery and a window through which towers and ships are visible. Inner border of bands; outer spearhead and band border. All in black and gold.

The Dutch composition, which also appears on a Delft plate, is possibly after an engraving by Bernard Picart (1673–1733), a French artist who worked in Amsterdam.[90] A covered creamer in the Liebman collection is also decorated with a design based on a Picart engraving (cat. no. 78). This design on this plate has been simplified from a more elaborate version of about 1745. As on a teabowl, coffee cup, and saucer decorated with the Agony in the Garden (cat. no. 105), gold has been generously applied, not used only as a highlight.

A color illustration of a plate decorated with the same subject is in Phillips, color pl. 9; also a tea service with the same subject, pl. 58. An earlier cup and saucer with the Embroideress in color and from a different source is in *Mottahedeh*, vol. 2, 271.

88
SOUP PLATE, molded rim
Indian market, ca. 1760
Diam. 9½ in. (24.1 cm.)
1975.97

Central scalloped cartouche with mahout dressed in orange, puce, and green, and holding a whip, astride a sepia elephant with a gold and iron-red saddle blanket. The elephant stands on a green ground between two grisaille rocks from which flowers sprout. Surrounding the cartouche is a vine pattern with large flowers in white on white. Gold engrailed inner border with dot points; white-on-white outer border with alternating lotus flowers and buds accented in puce, blue, green, and gold.

The subject of mahout and an elephant appeared with several border designs between 1760 and 1790 and was popular well into the nineteenth century.[91]

Illustration of matching plate in *Reeves Collection*, fig. 10; of matching platter in *Oriental Lowestoft*, pl. XII.

89
PLATE, notched octagonal rim
European market, ca. 1760
Diam. 9 in. (22.8 cm.)
1974.68
See color plate VI, page 15

Central scene of the Building of the Temple of Solomon, with King Solomon, Hiram, and Masonic symbols. All in blue, puce, iron red, chartreuse, yellow, brown, and gold. Gold line, inner border outlined in black. Outer spearhead border.

This design exemplifies a biblical theme later adapted to the traditions of Freemasonry. King Solomon and

Hiram—a Phoenician mastersmith sent by the king of Tyre—review plans for a temple for which Hiram is to do all the bronze work. The tools shown in the foreground became Masonic symbols. The same scene appears on a teabowl with the original arms of the Masons' Company about 1760.[92] The context of the Liebman plate, however, is purely pictorial.

90
PUNCH BOWL
Probably English market, ca. 1765
Diam. 14¹/₈ in. (36.1 cm.)
1974.85

On two sides: a scrolled cartouche with a hunt scene in puce, mauve, blue, iron red, yellow, green, sepia, and grisaille; on the other two sides: a smaller cartouche depicting birds on branches framed in gold bamboo with buds. Y-shaped cell-diaper ground in gold, black, and iron red. Gold vine border on footrim. On interior: two rows of black and iron-red hexagonal honeycombs edged by black and gold bands; continuous border of gold scrollwork on an iron-red ground alternating with gold cartouches with mauve cell-diapers and purple fish-scales, from which are suspended shells, flowers, and leaves. In center: scene of a hunter with dogs in a landscape enclosed by a medallion with a row of cell-diapers, gold and black bands, and spearheads.

The design source for this punch bowl is a set of engravings after James Seymour (1702–52), possibly by Thomas Burford (ca. 1710- ca. 1754), about 1753.[93] A hunt bowl was also brought back on the first American ship that entered the China trade in 1784, the *Empress of China.*[94] This suggests that such bowls were popular for use after the hunt in America as well as in England.

Illustration of matching bowl in catalogue of Sotheby, Parke-Bernet, January 30, 1975, 175; of bowl with similar scenes in *Mottahedeh*, vol. 1, pl. 280.

91
TEAPOY, molded gold scrollwork on
  base
European market, ca. 1765
H. 5¼ in. (13.4 cm.)
1975.128 a, b

Continuous scene of a wild-boar hunt, with hunters on horseback and hunting dogs. All in grisaille, shades of green, yellow, brown, iron red, blue, puce, and gold. Matching cover with spotted hunting dog and tree.

The scene portrayed is of a boar and not a fox hunt, as seen on a large punch bowl in the Liebman collection (cat. no. 90). The barefoot horsemen are all dressed in caps that might be Indian,

Near Eastern, or Russian. Perhaps the original for this scene was an engraving after a traveler's sketchbook or a classical Italian engraving.[95] The ovoid-shaped teapoy was popular from 1735 to 1770. For another example of this shape in the Liebman collection, see catalogue number 103.

Illustration of matching teapoy in *Mottahedeh*, vol. 1, pl. 281.

92

TEABOWL and SAUCER
Continental, probably French, market,
    ca. 1765
Teabowl: Diam. 3 in. (7.6 cm.)
Saucer: Diam. 4⅝ in. (11.9 cm.)
1975.101 a, b

Scene of lovers embracing in a wood
with Cupid overhead holding a torch
and wreath. They are surrounded by floral garlands. All in iron red. Gold rim.
Very finely potted.

This unidentified scene is possibly
after François Boucher (1703–70).
Although scenes from Boucher and
Antoine Watteau were popular on both
Chinese export porcelain and European

ceramics, the same scenes do not generally appear on both.[96] The coloring is
taken from engravings done in the style
of pastels.

Illustration of matching teabowl
and saucer in Gordon, 33, fig. 5. For a
simplified version of the scene without
Cupid, see a teapoy in *Mottahedeh*, vol.
2, pl. 352.

93
TRAY, molded rim
Probably French market, ca. 1765
L. 11 in. (28 cm.); W. 8½ in. (21.5 cm.)
1974.58

Central gold-edged medallion entwined with mauve ribbon depicting a hunter with his dog addressing a woman seated under a tree. She holds a cage in one hand and a string attached to a bird in the other. The couple is watched by a male figure hiding in the tree. All in green, blue, white, mauve, iron red, black, and sepia. Inner border of mauve ribbon festoons suspended by gold rings from a gold line. Mauve guilloche outer border between gold lines edged in mauve. Gold rim.

Both the decoration and shape of this piece are French in origin. The composition was inspired by a print by Jean-Michel Moreau le Jeune (1741–1814), about 1760.[97] The shape is similar to that of silver dish by Pierre Dumont le Jeune, dating about 1759 to 1760.[98] It became popular on English ceramics in the 1760s, when the Derby factory copied a similar square shape dating to about 1752 from the Vincennes/Sèvres factory in France, and was also popular in Spain and Portugal from 1770 on. The Chinese export piece was probably not made before about 1765 because of the time it would have taken for both the shape and design to reach Guangzhou.

Illustration of matching plate in Beurdeley, cat. 127.

94
PLATE
English market, ca. 1765
Diam. 9 in. (22.9 cm.)
1974.78

Central depiction of the Danby Gate entrance to the Oxford Botanical Garden, with Jacob Bobart, first superintendent, his pet goat and dog, and a stork overhead. All in grisaille and framed by a gold line outlined in black. Inner gold spearhead and cup border. Outer border of floral bouquets in puce, mauve, blue, yellow, iron red, sepia, turquoise, green, and chartreuse. Gold rim.

This scene represents the earliest complete view of the Danby Gate,

engraved in 1713 by the Dutch artist Michael Burgher as the frontispiece to a poem by Abel Evans entitled *Vertumnus, An Epistle to Mr. Jacob Bobart, Botany Professor to the University of Oxford, and Keeper of the Physick Garden*.[99] Bobart (1599–1680), who is bearded, is depicted on the left, with his pet goat and dog, both of which animals were associated with Asclepius, whom Bobart resembles. The inclusion of a stork suggests familiarity with Cesare Ripa's late sixteenth-century *Iconologia*, where it is an attribute of Aide, represented as a bearded man with a staff.

Plates with this design were probably ordered by John Bradby Blake (b. 1745), a supercargo of the East India

Company and member of the company's administrative council, for Humphrey Sibthorp (1713–97), who was Sherardian professor of botany at Oxford. Blake, a naturalist, shipped plant specimens back to England, as well as paintings of trees, fruits, and flowers, with his own annotations. At the time of his premature death in 1773, he was in England, having just delivered to Josiah Wedgwood "specimens of earth, clay, stone, sand, and other materials used in making the true Nankin porcelain."[100]

Illustration of matching plate in *Patterns*, 106, pl. 44; Miller, 99; and *Mottahedeh*, vol. 1, pl. 258.

95
PLATE
Dutch market, ca. 1780
Diam. 9⅛ in. (23.2 cm.)
1975.160

Central scene of the Cherry Pickers in puce, mauve, green, yellow, blue, sepia, iron red, white, and grisaille surrounded by a gold band edged in black. Outer guilloche border in gold and iron red.

The design source for the Cherry Pickers is an engraving by Nicolas Ponce (1746–1831) after a painting by Pierre-Antoine Baudouin (1723–69).[101] It was popular on both Chinese export and European porcelain. J. Kaendler (1706–75) used it as a model at Meissen.[102] In 1779 and 1780 the Dutch East India Company in Guangzhou ordered thousands of pieces of porcelain decorated with the Cherry Pickers and a guilloche border similar to the Liebman example.[103] A saucer with a less elaborate rendering of the same subject is also in the Liebman collection.

Illustration of matching plate in *Oriental Lowestoft*, pl. XV; Beurdeley, fig. 29; Scheurleer, cat. 214.

96
Pair of MINIATURE COFFEE CUPS,
   molded handle and rim
English market, ca. 1795
H. 2 in. (5 cm.)
1975.140 a, b

Continuous scene, Coming from School,
with children frolicking in mauve, brown,
green, and black. Upper border of gold
and blue bands with gold double-dot
pendants; gold and blue dot border
along interior rim.

The design is probably from an
engraving by Peltro W. Tomkins (1760–
1840) after a painting by Thomas
Stothard (1755–1834).[104] Four of the children in the Stothard painting can be
seen on each of these cups.

Illustration of matching tea caddy
in Williamson, pl. XLI.

97
COFFEEPOT, lighthouse shape,
strawberry finial, entwined strap
handles with floral attachments
Western market, ca. 1795
H. 8½ in. (21.6 cm.)
1975.184 a, b

On each side: a black and gold floral
bouquet. Lower black leaf and gold dot
border. Upper interlaced border of a
black and gold leafy garland and black
ribbon. Matching lid.

The black decoration on this coffeepot is heavy and coarse compared to
the more finely painted grisaille decora-

tion of half a century earlier. Although
the lighthouse shape is ultimately
derived from a silver prototype, the handles and attachments are from Leeds
ceramic examples. This type of coffeepot was decorated in a variety of styles
especially popular for the American
market.

98
COVERED VEGETABLE DISH, orange
   and gold entwined handles, berry
   finial
European market, ca. 1800
L. 12¼ in. (31.2 cm.); W. 9 in. (22.8 cm.)
1975.119 a, b

On each side: a sepia and gold European landscape with boats enclosed by
a black banded medallion with flowers
in green, iron red, puce, and blue.
Lower blue sawtooth border; upper
black band with flowers; gold engrailed

and blue dot border.
   The shape of this vegetable dish
was popular until about 1805. Similar
Western landscapes appear on a
lighthouse-shaped coffeepot in the
Liebman collection (cat. no. 99).

99
COFFEEPOT, lighthouse shape,
    entwined strap handles with
    gold floral attachments, gold berry
    finial
Probably American market, ca. 1800–05
H. 9¼ in. (23.5 cm.)
1975.120 a, b

On each side: medallion edged in gold enclosing a Western landscape in sepia. Lower gold and iron-red husk border. Wide upper border with blue dot pendants suspended from gold C-scrolls; orange band with gold vine; blue band with gold leaves. Gold band on spout. Matching lid.

A wide enamel band with several

border variations was common on porcelain for the American market from about 1790 to 1810. This coffeepot would have been part of a large tea and coffee service. Medallions with Western landscapes also appear on a contemporary vegetable dish in the Liebman collection (see cat. no. 98).

100

COVERED FLAGON, entwined strap
　　handles with gold and blue floral
　　attachments, gold Fo-dog finial
Probably American market, ca. 1800–05
H. 11 in. (27.9 cm.)
1975.183 a, b

On either side: large gold and blue floral
bouquet; smaller bouquet below spout.
Lower and upper blue band borders
with gold vine highlighted in iron red.
　　This late vine border was popular
into the nineteenth century and appears

in combination with a variety of central
scenes. The simplicity of the decoration
on this flagon was probably to keep the
cost down. Flagons with more elaborate
decoration are known.

101

PLATE, valanced rim
Probably Dutch market, ca. 1720
Diam. 8½ in. (21.7 cm.)
1974.75

Central scene of the Baptism of Jesus. Wide outer border of garlands, fruit, and flowers, supported at top by a bird and on sides by two putti. Below, two putti hold a banner inscribed MAT 3.16. All in iron red and gold.

It has been suggested that the spontaneous style of the painted decoration was copied directly from late seventeenth-century Protestant Dutch or English pottery painted with biblical scenes.[105] Here the scene of the Baptism is combined with a border found on a Delft plate of Jacob's Dream, dating about 1675–80.[106] The color choice of iron red and gold is in keeping with the color palette popular on armorial porcelain for the European market between 1720 and 1735. The Baptism of Jesus and Anointing of Saul were the only biblical subjects to appear on Chinese porcelain before 1740.

Color illustration of matching plate in *Reeves Collection*, pl. VI; *Oriental Lowestoft*, pl. XIV; Scheurleer, cat. 237. Matching plates with border variations illustrated in Phillips, pl. 54; Beurdeley, cat. 226; *Patterns*, fig. 32; *Mottahedeh*, vol. 1, pl. 309.

102
TEABOWL, eggshell porcelain
European market, ca. 1740
Diam. 3 in. (7.7 cm.)
1974.71

Scene of Eve handing Adam the apple, surrounded by animals, rocks, and trees. All very delicately painted in grisaille with flesh tones. Gold scroll band interior border with flowers outlined in iron red. In center: iron-red flower highlighted with gold.

The lively painting on this delicately potted teabowl gives Adam, Eve, and the animals a particular appeal.

Whether this popular subject was intended as religious or erotic is uncertain. The gold scroll band on the interior of the teabowl was used in combination with central scenes on armorial porcelain from 1740 to 1750.

Illustration of matching teapot in Beurdeley, cat. 57; *Mottahedeh*, vol. 1, pl. 300.

103
TEAPOY, eggshell porcelain, scroll base
   with traces of gold
European market, ca. 1790
H. 4 in. (10 cm.)
1975.110

Continuous Oriental landscape with scene of a shepherd dressed in puce and blue robes talking to a young woman dressed in puce and pale turquoise, while Cupid shoots an arrow from a nearby tree. A basket of fruit is on the woman's left. All in grisaille, iron red, and gold. Upper grisaille floral scroll border, with gold, pale blue, and puce highlights.

The subject matter for this tea ser-vice is probably biblical, perhaps a version of Jacob and Rebecca (Genesis 29:1–12), but the actual print used by the Chinese artist has not been identified. Why Cupid would appear in a biblical scene, however, is unclear. A matching teabowl is also in the Liebman collection (not illustrated). The original porcelain lid of the teapoy has been replaced with one of silver.

104
SAUCER, eggshell porcelain
European market, ca. 1745
Diam. 6⅛ in. (15.4 cm.)
1974.57

Central scene probably of the Parable of the Talents. Inner gold line border. Leafy C-scroll border with flowers. All in grisaille, heightened with gold.

This scene probably represents the Parable of the Talents (Matthew 25:14–31) at the point where the third servant, who had hidden the one talent given him by his master instead of doubling its value, accuses his master of reaping where he has not sown, and the master replies angrily that the servant is slothful and wicked (Matthew 25:24–26).

The border is of continental origin, similar in feeling to other examples from 1740–55.

105
TEABOWL and SAUCER, eggshell
   porcelain, and COFFEE CUP
European market, ca. 1745
Teabowl: Diam. 2¾ in. (7.0 cm.)
Saucer: Diam. 4½ in. (11.4 cm.)
Coffee cup: H. 2⅝ in. (6.5 cm.)
1974.56 a, b; 1974.73

Central scene of the Agony in the Garden with the disciples asleep on the left
and Jesus standing on the right. All in
grisaille with gold foliage and iron-red
flesh tones. Gold rim.

This scene is also known as the
central design on an armorial service. It
has been described as a shepherd and
sleeping nymphs.[107] The following biblical identification, however, seems more
likely: "And when he rose up from
prayer, and was come to his disciples,
he found them sleeping for sorrow"
(Luke 22:45–6). As on the plate depicting the Embroideress (cat. no. 87), gold

is freely used to color entire areas, such
as the foliage. This treatment is a sign of
quality and is in keeping with the delicate eggshell porcelain. Although the
coffee cup is of different proportions
and less finely potted than the teabowl,
it would have shared the same saucer
nonetheless, since the eighteenth-
century custom was to ship twenty-four
teabowls, twenty-four coffee cups, and
only twenty-four saucers.

Illustration of the same scene on
plate with an ornate border in Gordon,
26, fig. 9.

106
PLATE
Continental market, ca. 1745
Diam. 8⁷/₈ in. (22.7 cm.)
1974.81

Central scene of the Crucifixion, with Jesus and two thieves in the center; soldiers with spears raised on the left; John the Baptist on the right; the three Marys and a crowd behind; and soldiers throwing dice for Jesus' coat in the foreground. Gold line inner border; wide outer border of strapwork, garlands, leaves, and ribbons. All in grisaille and gold.

The sudden appearance on export porcelain of a series of religious scenes, including the Nativity, the Crucifixion, the Ascension, the Descent from the Cross, and the Resurrection, with a

variety of interchangeable borders developed by the Meissen and Viennese du Paquier factories, suggests that around 1740 German and Austrian missionaries brought engravings of religious subjects to China to be copied. An identical scene of the Crucifixion in brilliant colors with a du Paquier border appears on another plate in the Liebman collection (cat. no. 107).

Illustration of matching plate in *Mottahedeh*, vol. 1, pl. 312. Illustration of this border on plate with the Resurrection in Beurdeley, cat. 228; Phillips, pl. 8; Du Boulay, fig. 118.

107
PLATE
Continental market, ca. 1750
Diam. 8⁷⁄₈ in. (22.3 cm.)
1974.69
See color plate VII, page 16

Central scene of the Crucifixion, with Jesus and two thieves in the center; soldiers with spears raised on the left; John the Disciple on the right; the three Marys and a crowd behind; and soldiers throwing dice for Christ's coat in the foreground. All in mauve, puce, blue, iron red, sepia, gold, shades of green, yellow, and grisaille. Inner gold line border. Wide outer border of cartouches with trelliswork, strapwork with leaves, cornucopiae, and leafy garlands. Gold line at rim.

This scene of the Crucifixion is identical to the grisaille version (cat. no. 106). Here it is combined with a versatile border that also appears on a plate with a central scene of the Nativity in grisaille (cat. no. 108), and on a pseudo-armorial coffeepot in puce (cat. no. 42). This Viennese du Paquier border was clearly a stock pattern used for a variety of central subjects in any number of hues. In its colorful depiction of a religious subject, this plate resembles two polychrome coffee cups in the Liebman collection (cat. no. 110). Although tea and coffee services with religious themes are known, it has been suggested that the series of plates decorated with the Crucifixion, the Resurrection, the Ascension, the Nativity, and the Descent from the Cross were not part of dinner services, but rather decorative pieces.[108]

Illustration of plate with the Crucifixion and matching border in Gordon, 29, fig. 4; of plate with the Resurrection and matching border in *Mottahedeh*, vol. 1, pl. 314.

108
PLATE
Continental market, ca. 1750
Diam. 8⅞ in. (22.4 cm.)
1974.82

Central scene of the Nativity. Inner line border. Wide outer border of cartouches with scales, strapwork, leaves, cornucopiae, and leafy garlands. All in black, heightened in gold. Gold rim.

The artist's use of hatched lines suggests that the model for this design was an engraving. The scene of the Nativity is also known with a cup-and-ball border like that on a creamer with the Resurrection (cat. no. 109).

Illustration of matching plate in *Patterns*, pl. 29; *L'Armoire hollandaise*, pl. 59; of matching tea caddy in Beurdeley, cat. 225; of color version in Palmer, fig. 40b.

109
CREAMER, scroll-shaped handle with
    molded hearts
European market, ca. 1745
H. 4⅞ in. (12.3 cm.)
1974.74

Under spout: the Resurrection, with
angel on left and Roman soldiers in foreground. All in grisaille, heightened with
gold. Gold cup-and-ball border outlined
in grisaille.

The Resurrection depicted on this
creamer with the cup-and-ball border is
also known with a du Paquier border
similar to that on a plate with the Cruci-

fixion (cat. no. 107). In the 1740s the cup-
and-ball border was used for armorial
services, as well as for services with
nonreligious Western decoration.

Illustration of Resurrection with
different border (similar to cat. no. 108)
in Phillips, pl. 8; Beurdeley, cat. 228;
Mottahedeh, vol. 1, pl. 313.

110
Pair of COFFEE CUPS
European market, ca. 1750
H. 2½ in. (6.3 cm.)
H. 2⅝ in. (6.6 cm.)
1974.80 a, b

Scene of the Ascension in puce, blue, iron red, mauve, sepia, green, black, and yellow. Gold line edged in iron red at rim.

Although the Ascension appears in color and without a border on these cups, it is also known in grisaille with a

border similar to that on the Nativity plate (cat. no. 108). It is possible that the border was left off the cups for lack of space.

Illustration of matching saucer in Scheurleer, cat. 239.

III
TEABOWL and SAUCER, eggshell
    porcelain, and SPOON TRAY
Continental market, ca. 1740
Teabowl: Diam. 3 1/8 in. (8 cm.)
Saucer: Diam. 4 3/4 in. (12 cm.)
Spoon tray: L. 4 7/8 in. (12.6 cm.); W. 3 1/8
    in. (7.9 cm.)
1975.138 a, b; 1975.150

Central scene traditionally identified as
Juno and the Peacock. Border of cartouches with scalework, quilting, and
peacocks interwoven with floral garlands. All in black, heightened in gold.
The figures of Juno and the Peacock also
appear in the center of the teabowl.

Juno and the Peacock was a popular mythological subject on Chinese
export porcelain although the design
source is unknown. The European scroll
and latticework border with peacocks
was used exclusively for services
painted in grisaille, although it was not
limited to those with mythological

designs. It was used on armorial services between 1740 and 1755, but even
more on services without arms. Because
a source for the border has not been
found in Hausmaler or du Paquier
designs, it is possible that the design
may originate in book illustration.[109]

Spoon trays were commonly used
until about 1790, even though saucers
were provided. The lobed-hexagonal
shape of the spoon tray, also popular
for tea stands, was indigenous to China.

A coffee cup with the same
design is also in the Liebman collection
(not illustrated).

112
PLATE
Continental market, ca. 1745
Diam. 9 in. (22.9 cm.)
1974.61

Central scene of the Judgment of Paris in iron red, green, puce, black, white, blue, and gold. Gold line inner border outlined in iron red. Puce European shell and scroll outer border.

The Judgment of Paris was possibly copied from a popular engraving by Marcantonio Raimondi (ca. 1480–1530).[110] The same scene was also popular on European porcelain, and an example painted in Holland shows the goddesses fully clothed.[111] The border, which is derived entirely from European baroque and rococo scroll motifs, was popular between 1745 and 1755.

Illustration of similar plate in Beurdeley, cat. 130; in Gordon, pl. XIV; of an earlier plate with different border in *Mottahedeh*, vol. 1, pl. 304.

113

Pair of COFFEE CUPS
European market, ca. 1745
H. 2 3/8 in. (6 cm.)
1975.129 a, b

Scene of classical warrior in helmet with spear and shield, standing over a female warrior whose helmet, spear, and shield lie on the ground beside her. The warrior looks toward Cupid, who, encouraged by Venus, shoots two love birds toward him from the goddess's chariot. All in grisaille, heightened with gold. Gold and black rim.

Although this scene has been tentatively identified as Minerva and a resting youth,[112] it is possible that the sub-

ject represented on this pair of cups is the story of Achilles and Penthesilea, Queen of the Amazons, who came to the aid of Troy after Hector's death. Achilles fell in love with Penthesilea as he killed her. By mourning her excessively, Achilles revealed his love, only to be admonished by Thersites, whom he then killed.[113]

Illustration of matching coffee cup in Scheurleer, cat. 302; of teapot in *Mottahedeh*, vol. 1, pl. 333.

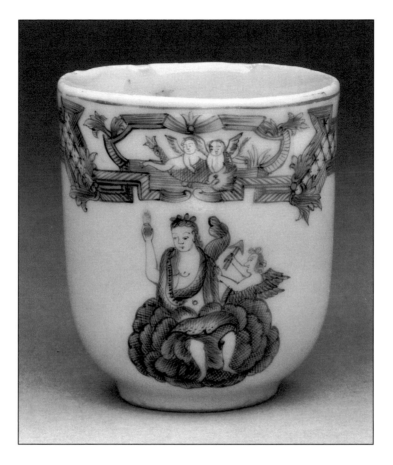

114
COFFEE CUP
Continental market, ca. 1745
H. 2½ in. (6.3 cm.)
1975.135 b

Figure of Jupiter on cloud with gold thunderbolt in his right hand; a snake, his attribute, around his shoulders; and a winged figure with gold arrow on his left. Border of cartouches with winged figures on a dolphin, birds, and trellis-work. At handle, a wreath and ribbon. All in grisaille, heightened in gold.

Both the borders and treatment of the mythological subject on this coffee cup resemble those on the teabowl, saucer, and spoon tray (cat. no. 111). In place of Juno and the Peacock, however, is Jupiter brandishing a thunderbolt. The border here is similar to that on the teabowls for Woodward (cat. no. 11).

115
COVERED CREAMER
Continental market, ca. 1750
H. 4⁷/₈ in. (12.4 cm.)
1975.99 a, b

Scene with two mythological figures seated together on a river bank beneath a tree. They are watched by a shepherd seated on a mountain on the other bank. All in brilliant shades of puce, green, blue, brown, yellow, and sepia. Gold rim. Matching landscape on cover.

A possible source for this design is an engraving by the Count of Caylus after a lost painting attributed to Watteau entitled *Acis et Galatée*. According to myth, Galatea loved Acis and therefore spurned the attention of the cyclops Polyphemus. When Polyphemus caught Acis listening to a love song he was singing to Galatea, he killed Acis with a boulder. Galatea escaped by diving into the sea and turned Acis into a river as the boulder crushed him.[114] The date of both the engraving and painting is unknown, but the painting is mentioned along with the name of the engraver Joullain (perhaps erroneously) in a sale by Charles-Antoine Coypel in 1753.[115] The minor differences between the creamer and the engraving may be due to the copyist's carelessness.

116
PLATE
European market, ca. 1750
Diam. 9⅛ in. (23.1 cm.)
1975.170

Central scene of Aurora in her chariot being drawn across the sky by two winged horses. Inner spearhead border; four border panels framed in iron red and gold, two with scenes of doves, and two with hunting dogs. All in grisaille, heightened with gold. Iron-red rim.

That the design for this mythologi-cal scene derives from an engraving is indicated by the use of hatched lines. Both the subject of Aurora and similar border panels occur separately on examples of armorial porcelain about 1745.

Illustration of armorial plate with same central scene in Howard, 334.

117
TEAPOT
European market, ca. 1750
H. 5¼ in. (13.3 cm.)
1975.141 a, b

On each side: the figure of Ceres with foliage in her hair, holding a sickle in her left hand and standing upon branches. Wide border of coronets above crossed batons, leaves, floral festoons, cornucopiae, and ribbons. All in grisaille, heightened with gold. Matching lid.

The awkwardly drawn female figure probably represents Ceres, although she looks more youthful than matronly. The same grisaille border is known in combination with central figures of other mythological goddesses, including Juno, as well as on services with personal monograms for the Swedish market. For other teapots in the Liebman collection with the same shape but different decoration, see figure 5 and catalogue number 74.

Illustration of matching saucer in Palmer, fig. 42.

118
JARDINIERE, fluted body, double
   handles, scalloped and molded rim
European market, ca. 1750–60
H. 8½ in. (21.6 cm.); Diam. 10 in. (25.4
   cm.) with handles
1975.94

On front and back: a central bouquet of
flowers; scattered smaller bouquets.
Lower floral scroll border. Continuous
upper border of *ruyi* motifs in alternating sizes, enclosing rosettes and single
cells and surrounded by floral sprays.
Floral garlands on handles. Bands at
rim. All in underglaze blue.

   The shape of this jardiniere, which
was also popular for ice pails, is derived
from a classical European silver
shape.[119] A jardiniere was both functional and decorative and made to
match a dinner service. Although the
molding is similar to that of the Gamon
and Elphinstone services (cat. nos. 23
and 24), the underglaze-blue border
decoration is only superficially similar.
The *ruyi* motifs derive from the head of
a Chinese ceremonial scepter.[120] Their
use here, however, is purely decorative.

   A similar jardiniere or ice pail is
illustrated in *Mottahedeh*, vol. 1, pl. 45.

INDIGENOUS EASTERN DESIGNS

About 1730 as the European demand for porcelain decorated with familiar Western designs increased, traditional Chinese motifs were eclipsed. Oriental decoration continued to appear, nevertheless, on a small amount of exportware destined for Europe, and by the end of the eighteenth century it once again became a dominant style. By this time, however, traditional Oriental designs had been tempered by years of European influence. Formerly symbolic design elements such as peonies, lotus blossoms, and Mandarin figures were now treated decoratively and arranged according to Western taste amid scrolled bands, scales, and intricate panels.[116] One such example in the Liebman collection is a platter made for Marie and De Witt Clinton about 1796 (cat. no. 62). It is decorated with figures of the Eight Immortals, traditionally the elite among the *xian* (men who leave society to live a solitary life of contemplation in the mountains). Here the figures have been removed from the wild, craggy landscape in which they appear in traditional Chinese art to become colorful elements in a bold, decorative Western pattern.[117]

Besides the Eight Immortals, the traditional symbols of the arts—chrysanthemums and peonies incorporating scrolls and vases—are also used on export porcelain in a purely decorative manner. Collectively known as Fitzhugh, several patterns with these design elements appear at different times in the mid-eighteenth and nineteenth centuries. To be accurate, only the version purchased in Guangzhou in 1780 by Captain Thomas FitzHugh should be accorded that name.[118] A redesign of an earlier Chinese pattern popular between 1765 and 1770, the service for Thomas FitzHugh was decorated in underglaze blue with four groups of flowers and emblems around a central Chinese motif, surrounded by a spearhead, dumbbell, and cell-diaper border. Another border design developed at Jingdezhen in the 1780s was an underglaze-blue band of butterflies, frets, and hexagonal cell-diapers, to the center of which enameled coats of arms could be added later in Guangzhou (see cat. nos 23 and 24). This same Jingdezhen border also appeared in combination with chrysanthemums and peonies incorporating scrolls and vases, surrounding not a medallion of Chinese motifs, but a pseudo-armorial device with a personal monogram (cat. no. 68) or an American eagle (cat. no. 67). These services, popular both in England and in America during the nineteenth century, were decorated not only in underglaze blue, but in iron-red, sepia, and overglaze green enamel (cat. no. 124).

Of Oriental origin and enthusiastically imitated in Europe were panels of Oriental figures in either a landscape or domestic scene. Known as chinoiseries, these scenes were copied onto Meissen porcelain by J. G. Herold as early as 1722. For the next decade, numerous artists at Meissen painted chinoiseries, combining them with borders developed at Meissen. These porcelains soon became so popular that they were sent back to China to be copied. A Meissen saucer and a Chinese export deep plate (fig. 11 and cat. no. 79) illustrate how Chinese figural and landscape scenes became part of the Western repertoire of patterns sent to China to be copied onto export porcelain for the Western market.

119
TEABOWL and SAUCER
European market, ca. 1755
Teabowl: Diam. 4³/₈ in. (10.9 cm.)
Saucer: Diam. 6³/₈ in. (16.1 cm.)
1975.125 a, b

Central gold floral bouquets enclosed within a medallion from which radiate puce lotus petals, with deeper puce veining. Gold foliate details edged in iron red between petals at rim. Matching teabowl with gold spearhead interior border outlined in iron red.

The lotus petal motif was popular on export porcelain and used in a variety of ways. Here it is stylized, yet sim-

ple, compared to an earlier use of lotus-shaped petals separated by swastika diapers to enclose pairs of figures (cat. no. 70). The gold floral bouquet inside the central medallion is similar to the flowers found on tobacco leaf patterns of the same period.

Illustration of matching bowl in *Reeves Collection*, fig. 13.

120
SHALLOW DISH
Probably Near Eastern market, ca. 1750
Diam. 8⅝ in. (22 cm.)
1991.344

Central floral design in pink and white overglaze enamels, surrounded by lotus petal design in underglaze-blue scrollwork with overglaze-pink and white enamels; outer underglaze-blue feathered border.

Both the lotus petal design and scrollwork appear on examples of Chinese exportware of about 1750, including pieces with French arms (see *Mottahedeh*, vol. 2, pl. 450). The design

itself is part Chinese and part Near Eastern. Because there are no exact Persian parallels, the dish may have been made for the Turkish rather than Persian market (*Mottahedeh*, vol. 2, 465). Another shallow dish in the Liebman collection has a rim in the shape of lotus petals and is painted in the *famille rose* palette (not illustrated).

Illustration of similar shallow dish in *Mottahedeh*, vol. 2, pl. 472.

121
SHALLOW BOWL
European market, ca. 1780
Diam. 10⁷/₈ in. (27.7 cm.)
1975.165

Central scene of Oriental figures in a landscape, all in puce, iron red, blue, shades of green, gold, white, and black. Wide border of mauve trelliswork above cartouches of gold diapers on an iron-red ground. Alternating blue and white cartouches edged in yellow above floral festoons and cartouches of iron-red Ori-ental landscapes. Iron-red and gold lines at rim.

The border of this shallow bowl is similar to that on the mug inscribed PETER CHAPMAM PARROTT (cat. no. 48) and is derived from Meissen. For other examples of scenes with Chinese figures, see catalogue number 122.

122

COVERED VEGETABLE DISH
European market, possibly English, ca.
 1795
L. 13 1/8 in. (34 cm.); W. 10 1/4 in. (26 cm.)
1975.162 a, b

On the sides of the vegetable dish and cover: a depiction of different Oriental scenes with figures. All finely painted in puce, mauve, iron red, sepia, blue, green, yellow, black, and gold. Iron-red band with gold meander pattern. Wide mauve trelliswork border interrupted by panels of iron-red Oriental landscapes alternating with panels of a robin on a branch in black and iron red on a white

ground. Wide outer gold leafy scroll border with reserves of alternating iron-red and sepia landscapes. Two matching platters and a vegetable dish are also in the Liebman collection (not illustrated).

Illustration of a matching dish belonging to an English family in Gordon, 74, fig. 3; illustration of pattern with an added coat of English arms in Howard, 346.

123
COVERED TUREEN, molded handles
    and berry finial in underglaze blue
Western market, ca. 1800
L. 14¾ in. (37.5 cm.); W. 9½ in. (24.1
    cm.).
1975.179 a, b

Traditional Fitzhugh pattern with central
medallion of Chinese motifs edged with
spearheads and dumbbells, surrounded
by four sprays of peonies and chrysanthemums incorporating scrolls and
vases. Lower cell-diaper border with
spearheads and dumbbells. All in underglaze blue.

The component parts of the
Fitzhugh pattern readily adapt to the
shape of the tureen, but their set place-

ment gives the pattern a rigidity despite
the lavishness of the design.[121] For a
plate in the Liebman collection with the
Fitzhugh pattern, see catalogue number
124. The Leeds creamware prototype for
this tureen is decorated with a molded,
feathered edge. Chinese export tureens
with Fitzhugh sprays, a central medallion, and feathered, molded edge are
also known.

124
PLATE, concave rim
Western market, ca. 1800
Diam. 9¾ in. (24.9 cm.)
1975.154

Fitzhugh pattern with central medallion of diapers and reserves of flowers edged with spearheads. The center has been left blank for a monogram. Surrounding are four bouquets of peonies and chrysanthemums incorporating scrolls and vases. Inner cell-diaper border interrupted by four reserves of flowers and vines. Outer border with cell-diapers, scales, butterflies, and frets. All in iron red.

This iron-red Fitzhugh plate was made as a stock pattern to be decorated later with a personal monogram or crest. Iron-red Fitzhugh services have been found in America as well as in Macao, suggesting that Fitzhugh designs were exported to several markets.[122] For another Fitzhugh pattern in the Liebman collection, see catalogue number 122.

Illustrations of iron-red Fitzhugh patterns with American eagles in Phillips, pl. 105; Mudge, fig. 63; and the *Reeves Collection*, pl. III, no. 3.

Endnotes

1 For the information in this section I am indebted to Clare Le Corbeiller, *China Trade Porcelain: Patterns of Exchange* (New York: The Metropolitan Museum of Art, 1974), 1–9; hereafter cited as *Patterns*, and to John Goldsmith Phillips, *China-Trade Porcelain* (Cambridge, MA.: Harvard University Press, 1956), 17–22; hereafter cited as Phillips.

2 *The Burghley Porcelains*, ed. Alexandra Munroe and Naomi Noble Richard (New York: Japan Society, 1986), 59.

3 See D. F. Lunsingh Scheurleer, *Chinese Export Porcelain: Chine de Commande* (New York: Pitman Publishing Corp., 1974), 163; hereafter cited as Scheurleer. The designs of Dutch artist Cornelis Pronk (1691–1759) are discussed and illustrated in David Howard and John Ayers, *China for the West: Chinese Porcelain and Other Decorative Arts for Export Illustrated from the Mottahedeh Collection*, vol. 1 (Totowa, NJ: Sotheby Parke Bernet Publications, 1978), 292–305; hereafter cited as *Mottahedeh*. This comprehensive work describes a number of pieces also in the Liebman collection.

4 Hunter is quoted at length in David Sanctuary Howard, *Chinese Armorial Porcelain* (London: Faber and Faber, 1974), chapter two; hereafter cited as Howard. For a description of the *hang*, see also Carl L. Crossman, *The China Trade* (Princeton, NJ: The Pyne Press, 1972), 3; hereafter cited as Crossman.

5 Hunter, in Howard, 21–22.

6 Crossman, 9.

7 Pickman, in Crossman, 9–10.

8 Scheurleer, 64–65, discusses in detail the hazards of special-ordering porcelain from Jingdezhen.

9 Phillips, 28.

10 Phillips, 28.

11 Hunter, in Howard, 22.

12 Quoted in Michel Beurdeley, *Chinese Trade Porcelain*, trans. Diane Imber (Rutland, VT: Charles E. Tuttle, 1962), 64, hereafter cited as Beurdeley.

13 Conrad Edick Wright, "Merchants and Mandarins: New York and the Early China Trade," in David Sanctuary Howard, *New York and the China Trade* (New York: The New-York Historical Society, 1984), 30; hereafter cited as Howard, *New-York*.

14 See Leonard Whiter, *Spode: A History of Family, Factory and Wares from 1733–1833* (London: Barrie and Jenkins, 1970), 71–72; hereafter cited as *Spode*.

15 *Patterns*, 84.

16 Callie Huger Efird and Katharine Gross Farnham, *Chinese Export Porcelain from the Reeves Collection*, (Lexington, VA: Washington and Lee University Press, 1973); hereafter cited as *Reeves Collection*.

17 *Patterns*, 117.

18 Jean McClure Mudge, *Chinese Export Porcelain for the American Trade 1785–1835*, 2nd rev. ed. (Cranberry, NJ: Associated University Presses, 1981), fig. 43; hereafter cited as Mudge.

19 Suzanne G. Valenstein, *A Handbook of Chinese Ceramics* (New York: The Metropolitan Museum of Art, 1975), 97. She further points out that the distinction between porcelain and porcelaneous stoneware is a very subtle one, 43.

20 Although one of the principal urban centers of China and one of the largest cities in the world, Jingdezhen was never granted the status of a city because it lacked an educated class. See Phillips, 2, for a full description of the city and the manufacture and decoration of porcelain at Jingdezhen.

21 Howard, 63.

22 Homer Eaton Keyes, "Quality in Oriental Lowestoft," *Antiques* (December 1937). Reprinted in *Chinese Export Porcelain*, ed. Elinor Gordon (New York: Main Street/Universe Books, 1975), 47; hereafter cited as Gordon.

23 See various examples from Leeds pattern books reproduced in Donald Towner, *English Cream-coloured Earthenware* (London: Faber and Faber, 1957).

24 His list of prices is reproduced in Mudge, Appendix II, 256–60. For a discussion of the shapes of export porcelain for the American market, see also Mudge, 150–55.

25 Mudge, 151.

26 Mudge, 152.

27 Howard, 67–68. His text is indispensable to any discussion of armorial porcelain, as is his pictorial guide to dating by border designs. I am also grateful to him for his help in dating specific pieces in the Liebman collection.

28 *Mottahedeh*, vol. 2, 379.

29 See Howard, Appendix XIII, which analyzes book-plate originals for Chinese armorial porcelain.

30 *Reeves Collection*, 39.

31 Phillips, 17.

32 Sir Algernon Tudor-Craig, *Armorial Porcelain of the Eighteenth Century* (London: Century House, 1925); hereafter cited as Tudor-Craig.

33 Tudor-Craig, 75.

34 Phillips, 110.

35 Clare Le Corbeiller, *China Trade Porcelain: A Study in Double Reflections* (New York: China Institute in America, 1973); hereafter cited as *Double Reflections*.

36 Solla, Conde de Castro, *Ceramica Branzonada*, 2 vols. (Lisbon, 1928); hereafter cited as *Ceramica Branzonada*.

37 *Ceramica Branzonada*, vol. 1, pl. XVII.

38 *Double Reflections*, 69.

39 Phillips, 121.

40 Howard, 147.

41 *Double Reflections*, 70.

42 *Patterns*, 112.

43 Marvin C. Ross, *Russian Porcelains* (Norman, OK: University of Oklahoma Press, 1968).

44 *Patterns*, 9.

45 Howard, 152.

46 Jean McClure Mudge, *Chinese Export Porcelain in North America* (New York: Crown Publishers/C.M. Potter Books, 1986); hereafter cited as *North America*.

47 J. A. Lloyd Hyde, *Oriental Lowestoft* (New York: Scribner's Sons, 1936); hereafter cited as *Oriental Lowestoft*.

48 Mudge, 178.

49 See Phillips, 172.

50 Ruth Ralston, "Some Sources of American Heraldic Decorations: Chinese Lowestoft and the Arms of New York and Rhode Island," *Antiques* 15 (January 1929): 43.

51 Illustrated in *Patterns*, pl. 41.

52 Scheurleer, 158; see also Phillips, 146.

53 Mudge, 172.

54 My thanks to Professor Dustin Cowell, University of Wisconsin–Madison, Department of African Languages and Literature, for the translation of the Arabic inscriptions.

55 See *North America*, 133–34.
56 Scheurleer, 31–32.
57 Mudge, 172–73.
58 Illustrated in Phillips, fig. 22; Beurdeley, cat. 208.
59 See Mudge, 168.
60 See Charles Oman, *English Domestic Silver*, 4th ed. (London: Adams and Charles Black, 1959), pl. XXIX, no. 90.
61 See *Spode*, 110.
62 See *North America*, 222.
63 Cecile and Michel Beurdeley, *Giuseppe Castiglione: A Jesuit Painter at the Court of the Chinese Emperors*, trans. Michael Bullock. (Rutland, VT: Charles E. Tuttle, 1972), 16.
64 Phillips, 60–61.
65 See *Patterns*, 9, for a full discussion of European designs brought to Guangzhou. Howard, 132, points out that if armorial porcelains in grisaille were painted in Guangzhou, it follows that Western subjects in grisaille would have been painted there as well.
66 *Patterns*, 8.
67 See Scheurleer, 97–98 and *Patterns*, 31–32 for a full explanation of events. Illustration in Scheurleer, cat. 131 and *Patterns*, fig. 12.
68 Sir Harry Garner, *Oriental Blue and White* (London: Faber and Faber, 1970).
69 See *Mottahedeh*, vol. 1, 77–78.
70 For a full discussion of marks on Chinese export porcelain, see *North America*, 229–36.
71 *Mottahedeh*, vol. 1, 145; Scheurleer, 136–37; Beurdeley, 194.
72 D.F. Lunsingh Scheurleer, *L'Armoire hollandaise aux porcelaines de Chine* ([Paris: Les Presses Artistiques, 1971]); hereafter cited as *L'Armoire hollandaise*.
73 See W. B. Honey, *European Ceramic Art from the End of the Middle Ages to about 1815* (London: Faber and Faber, 1952), 300.
74 Scheurleer, 34.
75 *Mottahedeh*, vol. 1, 305.
76 *Patterns*, 64–65. The Herisset engraving is reproduced in fig. 27.
77 G. C. Williamson, *The Book of Famille Rose* (London: Methuen, 1927); hereafter cited as Williamson.
78 Arlene M. Palmer, *A Winterthur Guide to Chinese Export Porcelain* (New York: Rutledge Books, 1976); hereafter cited as Palmer.
79 See *Patterns*, figs. 51 and 52.
80 David Howard, "Chinese Porcelain of the Jacobites," pt. 1, *Country Life* (January 25, 1973): 243; hereafter cited as "Jacobites."
81 "Jacobites," 243; *Patterns*, 94.
82 *Mottahedeh*, vol. 1, 239–40.
83 See Phillips, 132, for a discussion of a plate with this subject matter; the original engraving is reproduced in fig. 44.
84 See *Patterns*, 81–82; Beurdeley, 110.
85 *Mottahedeh*, vol. 1, 346.
86 Lancret's painting is illustrated in Scheurleer, cat. 217. See also 139.
87 Scheurleer, 182.
88 *Double Reflections*, 41.
89 The engraving is illustrated in Scheurleer, cat. 207. See also 221.
90 See Phillips, 132; and Scheurleer, 126, 138–39.
91 See Phillips, pls. 107 and 108, and Mottahedeh, vol. 2, 478.
92 Illustrated in Howard, 333.
93 Beurdeley, 64.
94 See Mudge, fig. 43; Philip Chadwick Foster Smith, *The Empress of China* (Philadelphia: Philadelphia Maritime Museum, 1984), pls. 64, 65.
95 *Mottahedeh*, vol. 1, 283.
96 Scheurleer, 126.
97 Beurdeley, 178.
98 Faith Dennis, *Three Centuries of French Domestic Silver*, vol. 1. (New York: The Metropolitan Museum of Art, 1960), no. 444.
99 See B.D.H. Miller, "Oxford in Chinese Export Ware," *Oriental Art*, 12 (Summer 1966), 101; hereafter cited as Miller; and *Patterns*, 105–7 and fig. 57 for a full discussion of the iconography and history of the subject.
100 *Patterns*, 107.
101 See Beurdeley, figs. 27 and 28.
102 Anthony Du Boulay, *Chinese Porcelain*. (New York: Putnam, 1963), fig. 118; hereafter cited as Du Boulay.
103 Scheurleer, 138.
104 *Bryan's Dictionary of Painters and Engravers*, vol. 5 (London: G. Bell and Sons, Ltd., 1927), 133.
105 *Patterns*, 69.
106 *Patterns*, 69–70, figs. 32–33.
107 Gordon, 26.
108 *Mottahedeh*, vol. 1, 320.
109 *Mottahedeh*, vol. 1, 321.
110 Gordon, 25.
111 Beurdeley, cat. 131.
112 Scheurleer, 227, no. 302.
113 *Oxford Classical Dictionary*, 2nd ed., ed. N.G.L. Hammond and H. H. Scullard (Oxford: Clarendon Press, 1970), 798; hereafter cited as *OCD*.
114 *OCD*, 453.
115 Jean Ferré, *Watteau*, vol. 3 (Madrid: Athéna, 1972), 1008, B57.
116 *Reeves Collection*, 12.
117 See W. A. Thorpe, "Legend and Romance in Chinese Porcelain: The Eight Immortals," *Antiques* 23 (April 1, 1933): 139.
118 For a full discussion of the Fitzhugh pattern and illustrations, see Howard, 51–55 and 150–51; also J.B.S. Holmes, reprinted in Gordon, 156.
119 Beurdeley, 162.
120 Scheurleer, 193; *North America*, 250.
121 See *Reeves Collection*, 19.
122 Phillips, 201.

List of works cited

Beurdeley, Cecile and Michel. *Giuseppe Castiglione: A Jesuit Painter at the Court of the Chinese Emperors*. Translated by Michael Bullock. Rutland, VT: Charles E. Tuttle, 1972.

Beurdeley, Michel. *Chinese Trade Porcelain*. Translated by Diane Imber. Rutland, VT: Charles E. Tuttle, 1962.

Bryan's Dictionary of Painters and Engravers. 5 vols. London: G. Bell and Sons, Ltd., 1927.

The Burghley Porcelains. Edited by Alexandra Munroe and Naomi Noble Richard. New York: Japan Society, 1986.

Crossman, Carl L. *The China Trade*. Princeton, NJ: The Pyne Press, 1972.

Dennis, Faith. *Three Centuries of French Domestic Silver*. 2 vols. New York: The Metropolitan Museum of Art, 1960.

Du Boulay, Anthony. *Chinese Porcelain*. New York: Putnam, 1963.

Efird, Callie Huger and Katharine Gross Farnham. *Chinese Export Porcelain from the Reeves Collection*. Lexington, VA: Washington and Lee University Press, 1973.

Ferré, Jean. *Watteau*. 4 vols. Madrid: Athéna, 1972.

Garner, Sir Harry. *The Arts of the Ch'ing Dynasty*. London: The Arts Council of Great Britain and the Oriental Ceramic Society, 1964.

Garner, Sir Harry. *Oriental Blue and White*, 3rd ed. London: Faber and Faber, 1970.

Gordon, Elinor. *Chinese Export Porcelain: A Historical Survey*. New York: Main Street/Universe Books, 1975.

Holmes, J.B.S. "Fitzhugh and FitzHughs in the China Trade," *Antiques* 89 (January 1966): 130–31.

Honey, W. B. *European Ceramic Art from the End of the Middle Ages to about 1815*. London: Faber and Faber, 1952.

Howard, David Sanctuary. *Chinese Armorial Porcelain*. London: Faber and Faber, 1974.

Howard, David Sanctuary. "Chinese Porcelain of the Jacobites I," *Country Life* (January 25, 1973): 289–90.

Howard, David Sanctuary. "Chinese Porcelain of the Jacobites II," *Country Life* (February 1, 1973): 243–44.

Howard, David Sanctuary. *New York and the China Trade*. New York: The New-York Historical Society, 1984.

Howard, David and John Ayers, *China for the West: Chinese Porcelain and Other Decorative Arts for Export Illustrated from the Mottahedeh Collection*, 2 vols. Totowa, NJ: Sotheby Parke Bernet Publications, 1978.

Hyde, J.A. Lloyd. *Oriental Lowestoft*. New York: Scribner's Sons, 1936.

Keyes, Homer Eaton. "Quality in Oriental Lowestoft," *Antiques* 32 (December 1937): 290–94.

Le Corbeiller, Clare. *China Trade Porcelain: A Study in Double Reflections*. New York: China Institute in America, 1973.

Le Corbeiller, Clare. *China Trade Porcelain: Patterns of Exchange*. New York: The Metropolitan Museum of Art, 1974.

Little, Frances. "America's East Indiamen and the China Trade," *Antiques* 15 (January 1929): 27–31.

Miller, B.D.H. "Oxford in Chinese Export Ware," *Oriental Art*, 12 (Summer 1966): 99–103.

Mudge, Jean McClure. *Chinese Export Porcelain for the American Trade 1785–1835*, 2nd rev. ed. Cranberry, NJ: Associated University Presses, 1981.

Mudge, Jean McClure. *Chinese Export Porcelain in North America*. New York: Crown Publishers, C.M. Potter Books, 1986.

Oman, Charles. *English Domestic Silver*, 4th ed. London: Adam and Charles Black, 1959.

Oxford Classical Dictionary, 2nd ed. Edited by N.G.L. Hammond and H. H. Scullard. Oxford: Clarendon Press, 1970.

Palmer, Arlene M. *A Winterthur Guide to Chinese Export Porcelain*. New York: Rutledge Books, 1976.

Phillips, John Goldsmith. *China-Trade Porcelain*. Cambridge, MA: Harvard University Press, 1956.

Ralston, Ruth. "Some Sources of American Heraldic Decorations: Chinese Lowestoft and the Arms of New York and Rhode Island," *Antiques* 15 (January 1929): 41–44.

Ross, Marvin C. *Russian Porcelains*. Norman, OK: University of Oklahoma Press, 1968.

Santos, Maria Mattos dos. *The Marks*. Lisbon: Livraria Sá da Costa Editôra, 1968.

Scheurleer, D.F. Lunsingh. *Chinese Export Porcelain: Chine de Commande*. New York: Pitman Publishing Corp., 1974.

Scheurleer, D.F. Lunsingh. *L'Armoire hollandaise aux porcelaines de Chine*. [Paris: Les Presses Artistiques, 1971].

Smith, Philip Chadwick Foster. *The Empress of China*. Philadelphia: Philadelphia Maritime Museum, 1984.

Solla, Conde de Castro. *Ceramica Branzonada*, 2 vols. Lisbon, 1928.

Thorpe, W. A. "Legend and Romance in Chinese Porcelain: The Eight Immortals," *Antiques* 23 (April 1933): 139–41.

Towner, Donald. *English Cream-coloured Earthenware*. London: Faber and Faber, 1957.

Tudor-Craig, Sir Algernon. *Armorial Porcelain of the Eighteenth Century*. London: Century House, 1925.

Valenstein, Suzanne G. *A Handbook of Chinese Ceramics*. New York: The Metropolitan Museum of Art, 1975.

Whiter, Leonard. *Spode: A History of the Family, Factory and Wares from 1733–1833*. London: Barrie and Jenkins, 1970.

Williamson, G. C. *The Book of Famille Rose*. London: Methuen, 1927.

ELVEHJEM MUSEUM OF ART STAFF

Russell Panczenko, Director
Lori DeMeuse, Account Specialist
Douglas DeRosa, Grant Writer
William Gilmore, Preparator
Juliet Gunkel, Marketing and Membership Manager
Kristine Hastreiter, Preparator
Anne Lambert, Curator of Education and Outreach
Corinne Magnoni, Assistant Director for Administration
Tilda Mohr, Secretary to the Director
Patricia Powell, Editor
Sandy Schweiger, Museum Shop Manager
Andrew Stevens, Assistant Curator of Prints, Drawings, and Photographs
Lucille Stiger, Registrar

Building Maintenance
Gordon Booth, Custodian
Melvin Geborek, Maintenance Mechanic
Michael Skinner, Custodian
Russell Thompson, Maintenance Mechanic

Building Security
Nancy Cozzens-Ellis, Securty Officer-lead
Stephan Flannagan, Security Officer
Mark Golbach, Security Officer
Michael J. Prissel, Security Officer
Mark Stallsmith, Security Officer
Theodore T. Tyler, Security Officer
Terry Wilson, Security Supervisor

ELVEHJEM MUSEUM OF ART COUNCIL

Exofficio Members
David Ward, Provost/Vice Chancellor
Donald W. Crawford, Dean, College of
   Letters and Science
Russell Panczenko, Director, Elvehjem Museum of Art
Andrew A. Wilcox, President, UW Foundation

Fixed-term Appointments
Elizabeth Pringle, Elvehjem Museum of Art League President
Gail Goode, Elvehjem Docent

Members-at-Large
Ineva Baldwin
Joyce Bartell, Secretary
Anne Bolz
James Carley
Jane Coleman
Elaine Davis
Marshall Erdman
Marvin Fishman
Walter Frautschi
Newman T. Halvorson
Edith Jones
Barbara Kaerwer
Jean McKenzie
Mrs. Frederick Miller
Fred Reichelt, Chairman
Bryan Reid
Donald P. Ryan
Roth Schleck
Fannie Taylor
Thomas Terry
Jane Werner Watson
Susan Weston

Madison Campus Faculty and Student Members
Prof. Frank Horlbeck, Department of Art History
Prof. Robert Krainer, School of Business
Prof. N. Wayne Taylor, Department of Art